CPMR Discussion Paper
14

Performance Measurement in the Health Sector

Michelle Butler

IPA
INSTITUTE OF PUBLIC
ADMINISTRATION

First published in 2000
by the Institute of Public Administration
57-61 Lansdowne Road
Dublin 4
Ireland

www.ipa.ie

British Library Cataloguing in Publication Data
A catalogue record for this book is available from the British
Library

ISBN 1 902448 37 5
ISSN 1393–6190

Cover design by Peanntrónaic, Dublin
Typeset by the Institute of Public Administration
Printed by ColourBooks, Dublin

CONTENTS

Foreword

This paper is the fourteenth in a series undertaken by the Committee for Public Management Research. The Committee is developing a comprehensive programme of research designed to serve the needs of the future developments of the Irish public service. Committee members come from the Departments of Finance, the Environment and Local Government, Health and Children, the Taoiseach, and Public Enterprise, and also from Trinity College Dublin, University College Dublin and the Institute of Public Administration.

This series aims to prompt discussion and debate on topical issues of particular interest or concern. The papers may outline experience, both national and international, in dealing with a particular issue. Or they may be more conceptual in nature, prompting the development of new ideas on public management issues. They are not intended to set out any official position on the topic under scrutiny. Rather, the intention is to identify current thinking and best practice.

We would very much welcome comments on this paper and on public management research more generally. To ensure that the discussion papers and wider research programme of the Committee for Public Management Research are relevant to managers and staff, we need to hear from you. What do you think of the issues being raised? Are there other topics you would like to see researched?

Research into the problems, solutions and successes of public management processes and the way organisations can best adapt in a changing environment has much to contribute to good management, and is a vital element in the public service renewal process. The Committee for Public Management Research intends to provide a service to people working in public organisations by enhancing the knowledge base on public management issues.

Eric Embleton, Chair
Committee for Public Management Research
Department of Finance

For further information or to pass on any comments please contact:

Pat Hickson
Secretary
Committee for Public Management Research
Department of Finance
Lansdowne House, Lansdowne Road
Dublin 4

Phone: (+353) 1 676 7571; Fax: (+353) 1 668 2182
E-mail: hicksonp@cmod.finance.irlgov.ie

or

Michelle Butler
Institute of Public Administration
Vergemount Hall
Clonskeagh
Dublin 6

Phone: (+353) 1 269 7011; Fax: (+353) 1 269 8644
E-mail: mwbutler@ipa.ie

General information on the activities of the Committee for Public Management Research, including this paper and others in the series, can be found on its world wide web site: www.irlgov.ie/cpmr; information on Institute of Public Administration research in progress can be found at www.ipa.ie.

Acknowledgements

This project could not have been completed successfully without the active co-operation of a range of individuals involved in the development of performance measurement in the Department of Health and Children, the eight health boards and members of the ERHA taskforce.

I would also like to thank Carolyn Gormley and Karen Isaac for their help in the preparation and presentation of the paper and the IPA's Publications Division for its production.

Responsibility for the content of the paper, however, rests with the author.

Michelle Butler
May 2000

Executive Summary

This paper provides an overview of the development of performance measurement in the Irish health sector, drawing on reported developments in other health systems. Performance measurement has considerable potential in health service management in enabling national priorities for health reform to be translated into organisational and individual objectives, to provide a focus on results, and to enhance accountability. The paper begins by positioning the development of performance measurement within the range of recent policy and legislative changes in the Irish health sector. Drawing on the international literature, four key aspects of performance measurement are identified, which form the framework for the study: developing performance measurement systems; measure definition and data collection; developing the use of performance data; and co-ordinating performance measurement. Performance measurement was also reviewed at the national system level, the organisation level and the individual level.

The range of approaches currently in place to measure performance is outlined, and includes:

- systems to monitor health outcomes and progress against strategic priorities at the national level, such as the Public Health Information System (PHIS) and strategy indicators used for the National Cancer Register

- systems to monitor the performance of programmes/service areas, such as the hospital inpatient enquiry system (HIPE) and datasets being developed for mental health services and intellectual disability services

- systems to monitor performance at the health board and agency level, such as integrated management returns (IMRs) and service plan indicators.

A comparative review was undertaken of the development of performance measurement systems in Australia, New Zealand, the United Kingdom, the USA and Canada. The report concludes that the focus of performance measurement across these countries is on improving health outcomes, improving the quality of care, achieving national priorities and reducing inequalities in health. The findings also suggest that performance measurement systems are largely evolving around:

- developing national frameworks to define standards of expected performance
- developing good measures and data collection systems
- building managerial capacity to manage performance.

The findings highlight the need for strong leadership in promoting the development of performance measurement and developing frameworks to ensure that health care providers comply with good performance standards. Currently, performance measurement tends to be focused around acute health care, but there is increasing interest in extending performance measurement to all parts of the health care system.

The report looks at the approach taken across countries to developing performance measures. The concepts of performance measured include health improvement/outcomes, effectiveness and quality, the patient orientation of services, access and financial/resource management. Similar concepts are seen in the range of measures currently being used in the Irish health service, although coverage appears patchy. The area that needs to be developed in particular in the Irish health sector is the patient-orientation of services. The types of measures used across countries include rates; averages; medians or means; proportions; costs; composite measures; and other measures of performance. Similar measures are currently used in the Irish system although composite measures have yet to be developed. In terms of the development of performance measures the findings emphasise the need to move beyond an emphasis on finance and activity towards more balanced sets of measures and to focus on generating information that is useful to decision-makers. The findings also highlight the need to shift the emphasis from compliance with processes to focusing on results, and that performance measures should relate to key objectives in order to drive strategy forward.

The report highlights the need to have good quality data available at all levels of the system to support performance measurement. In terms of collecting, aggregating and disseminating data it is reported that data management systems are largely underdeveloped and fragmented. The acute hospital sector is where performance measurement is most developed. The need for a co-ordinated approach to the development of data management systems across the health system is identified.

The findings suggest that data currently available on performance is under-utilised and focused mainly on controlling expenditure. A number of points are raised about how the use of data can be improved. The decision-usefulness of data is an important issue. Data must be relevant to users and at the correct level of detail. Data also needs to be timely and easily accessible to those who need it. In addition, the managerial culture needs to be receptive to the importance of basing decisions on performance data, individuals need to feel empowered, and the appropriate skills and expertise are required to be able to interpret data and use the findings constructively. Data must be reliable and individuals need to have confidence in using it. At the individual level it is suggested that performance measurement needs to be developed and linked to performance management and personal development planning. The research found that performance measurement at the individual level is largely underdeveloped.

The findings emphasise the need for improved co-operation and collaboration across the health sector in the development of performance measurement. A number of areas must be addressed in this regard, including the need for greater clarity in defining who is responsible for co-ordinating performance measurement across the system.

The report concludes that the key issues to be addressed are:

- clarifying responsibility for overall co-ordination of performance measurement
- extending performance measurement to all areas of the health system
- extending performance measurement to the individual level within organisations and linking it with performance management

- developing more balanced sets of performance measures and ensuring their relevance to stakeholders
- developing an integrated data management system
- ensuring that decision-makers at all levels of the system have the skills and competencies required to make the best use of data produced.

1

Introduction

1.1 Focus of the report

This report on performance measurement provides an overview of the range of current approaches and plans for further development for performance measurement in the Irish health sector. It aims to identify the key issues arising, to generate guidelines for the design and use of performance measurement systems, and to identify the essential elements of a framework for performance measurement in the health sector.

1.2 Background and context

PUMA/SBO (1999) suggest that performance management has considerable potential in public management as a vehicle for ensuring that the highest priorities of government are transformed into strategic outputs to be cascaded down throughout organisations. They also suggest that, coupled with the decentralisation of management authority in exchange for more explicit accountability, performance management has the potential to shift the emphasis in management from control and compliance with processes to strategic steering with a clear focus on results.

PUMA/SBO (1999) suggest that there are four key objectives to performance management systems:

- setting objectives and allocations for government actions
- establishing the types of authorities for carrying out those actions

- determining what information is needed to know that actions are executed properly

- rewards and sanctions for performance.

Thus it can be seen that performance measurement is a central feature of performance management in the public service. Performance measurement has a key role in supporting effective decision-making and enhancing accountability.

Over the past decade in Ireland there has been an explicit call for enhancing the accountability of the public service, for public servants to demonstrate the effectiveness and efficiency of the services they deliver, and for policy-makers to monitor and evaluate the outcomes of policy development. The need for the public sector to take performance management on board, including the development of performance measurement systems, was emphasised by the Taoiseach in 1999 (SMI Working Group on Financial Management, 1999). In the health sector, which annually accounts for approximately 17 per cent of public expenditure, a number of approaches to reform are centred on enhancing accountability and performance measurement.

1.2.1 The drive for greater accountability

One of the central tenets of the Strategic Management Initiative (SMI) is the devolution of accountability and responsibility from the centre to executive agencies. In the near future the role of the Department of Health and Children will become increasingly focused on policy development and overall control of expenditure, with explicit devolution of its current role in operational management to executive agencies. The purpose of devolution is to enable decisions to be made closer to those who use services, thus enabling services to be more responsive to the needs of users. Devolution is proposed within a framework that provides adequate and accurate information to inform decisions and enables decision-makers, managers and staff to be held accountable. For effective devolution in health, performance measurement systems are required that enable health boards and providers to demonstrate that they are fulfilling devolved functions and for the department to monitor the performance of the system against agreed objectives.

The three principles explicitly underpinning *Shaping a Healthier Future* (1994) – the government's strategy for the reform of Ireland's health system – are equity, quality of service and accountability. *Shaping a Healthier Future* identifies the need to demonstrate effectiveness and value for money to the taxpayer and the responsibility of those providing services to achieve agreed objectives. It sets out arrangements to improve legal and financial accountability and highlights weaknesses to be addressed in the current system:

> Many of the services are not sufficiently focused towards specific goals or targets and it is therefore difficult to assess their effectiveness; the information which would support this focusing is frequently unavailable or, if available, under-utilised. (*Shaping a Healthier Future*, 1994, p. 10)

Dixon and Baker (1996, p. 10), in their review of management across the Irish health system, 'detected an *absence of clear accountability* within the system, both between managers and their staff and between different levels in the system'. Their research identified a number of 'complex' reasons for the lack of organisational and individual accountability in the system.

Recent changes in legislation have the enhancement of accountability in public services – including the health sector – as a central focus. The Public Service Management Act, 1997 provides for ministerial accountability to government for the performance of functions of departments. It also outlines the responsibilities of secretaries general, which include ensuring that the resources of the department are used in accordance with the Comptroller and Auditor General (Amendment) Act, 1993, and examining means to improve the cost-effective delivery of public services provided by the department.

Specifically in health, the Health (Amendment) (No. 3) Act, 1996 refers to the need for health boards to 'secure the most beneficial, effective and efficient use' of resources. It outlines the role of the service plan in ensuring that health boards are accountable for the services provided and for related income and expenditure, and the responsibility of boards and chief executive officers (CEOs) for the supervision and implementation of the service plan. Also under the Act, health boards are required to produce and adopt an annual report that includes a statement of services provided.

The Comptroller and Auditor General (Amendment) Act, 1993 requires the Comptroller and Auditor General to audit the accounts of health boards, to include a review of whether the health board applied expenditure for the purpose for which it was intended, if transactions conformed to the correct authority, and if income and expenditure are supported by substantiating documentation. The Act also provides for the review of whether and to what extent resources were used, acquired or disposed of economically and efficiently and if disposals effected 'the most favourable terms reasonably obtainable'. It gives the Comptroller and Auditor General the right to access documents and information, to examine systems, procedures and practices, and to make comparisons as considered appropriate.

1.2.2 Measuring performance

Shaping a Healthier Future (1994) outlines a 'key' role for the Department of Health and Children in performance measurement, specifically in the evaluation of health boards against national objectives. It states that such evaluation should increasingly focus on the effectiveness of services, including quality, while 'embracing' economy and efficiency. It also identifies the need for health boards to put in place more structured arrangements to measure performance, both in their own organisations and in agencies with which they have service agreements.

There is a clear focus on performance measurement in the strategy statement document of the Department of Health and Children (the department) for 1998. In the document the department's mission includes '...ensuring that health and personal social services are planned, managed and delivered to achieve measurable health and social gain and to provide the optimum return on resources'. Three of the seven high-level objectives in the strategy statement articulate the dimensions of performance in the health system and suggest a growing emphasis on performance management:

- to encourage the attainment of the highest standards of effectiveness, efficiency, equity, quality and value for money in the health delivery system

- to strengthen accountability at all levels of the health service

- to optimise staff performance, training and development. (Department of Health and Children (DoHC), 1998, p. 8)

A number of issues relating to performance measurement are identified in the strategy statement. Firstly it is stated that one of the 'principal challenges' for the department in its evaluation and review function is:

the need to improve data systems and analysis, to develop evaluation and performance indicators, and to harness the rapid advances in information technology to best advantage. (DoHC, 1998, p. 11)

Secondly it raises as a priority the need to promote the service plan as the basis for ongoing discussion between the department and health boards and as a benchmark by which health board performance can be measured. In this sense it is stated that the challenge currently for health boards and agencies is to ensure that appropriate information is collected to enable effective evaluation and comparison. Thirdly, the need to build 'appropriate feedback mechanisms' is identified to enable reporting and feedback to become an integral part of the system and to allow the department to monitor its own progress against the objectives set out in the strategy statement. Fourthly, the ability to measure performance to support evaluation and corrective action and the strengthening of the finance function in health boards is outlined as the necessary precursor to the department devolving its functions and responsibilities to health boards.

The recently agreed Programme for Prosperity and Fairness (2000, p. 20) clearly links performance measurement with a strategic management approach to modernising the public service comprising:

- statement of strategy, *to inform a detailed*
- business/service planning, *to provide a means of*
- managing performance, *to improve the standard of*
- service delivery.

All of this suggests that performance measurement is highly topical in the health sector at present. Work is going on both within the department and in health boards and agencies. This study examines the range of approaches being developed and compares the findings with those from the literature on the development of performance measurement in other countries. A complementary study of performance measurement in local government was undertaken at the same time (see Boyle, 2000, CPMR Discussion Paper No. 15).

1.3 Terms of reference

The terms of reference of both studies were the same:

- to identify and outline current practice, both national and international, with regard to the development of performance measurement systems

- to explore the managerial and other issues which arise from the development and implementation of performance measurement systems, and develop guidelines for the design and use of measurement systems arising from this process

- to establish the essential elements of a framework for performance measurement, including the key criteria for performance indicator development.

While the two studies – of the local government and health sectors – cover much common ground, there are differences due to the distinct operational aspects of each sector. Common issues from the two studies have been summarised in a briefing paper (CPMR Briefing Paper No. 1, 2000).

1.4 Methodology

The study is based on interviews with a number of key individuals involved in the development of performance measurement, either within the Department of Health and Children, the health boards, the ERHA taskforce, or on collaborative working groups. It also involved a review of related documents in the Irish health sector and a review of the international health care literature.

1.5 Structure of the report

In Chapter 2 a framework is presented for performance measurement, which forms the basis for the research on performance measurement in the health sectors in Ireland and in a range of other countries. In Chapter 3, the first part of that framework is used to compare approaches to the development of performance measurement systems. In Chapter 4, issues around data definition and collection from an international perspective are discussed. Chapter 5 explores approaches to data definition and collection in the Irish health sector. Chapter 6 focuses on the use of performance data in decision-making and in Chapter 7, issues around the co-ordination of performance measurement are discussed. By way of conclusion, the key focus of Chapter 8 is the presentation of the essential elements of a framework for performance measurement and key considerations for performance indicator development.

2
A Framework for Performance Measurement

2.1 Introduction

In this chapter the framework for the research is outlined, drawing on the initial findings from the literature on the development of performance measurement in other countries. Some key issues concerning the practicalities of measuring performance are identified.

2.2 The development of performance measurement

In the public sector the potential benefits from performance measurement are gaining wider acceptance. PUMA (OECD, 1998) outlines a key role for performance measurement in the public sector to support decision-making, resulting in improved outcomes for the community and enabling organisations to meet external accountability requirements.

In a recent analysis of health care policy across OECD countries, Kalisch et al. (1998) report three dominant themes: (1) maximising quality of care and consumer satisfaction at minimum cost; (2) macroeconomic cost control; and (3) ensuring that citizens have access to treatment and health care based on their needs rather than ability to pay.

Other points raised by Kalisch *et al.* include the following.

• The need to shift the emphasis in health care from cure to prevention. Such a shift would need to be underpinned by an appropriate balance in the provision of primary care and acute hospital services.

- A growing acceptance that quality and efficiency need to go hand in hand. This is on the basis of concern in governments to protect vulnerable populations, and concerns that previous policy measures aimed at reducing costs alone had unacceptable impacts on access to care and increased customer dissatisfaction.

- Increasing concern about the effectiveness of health services and the impact of inefficiency, duplication of services and the lack of information and data systems on quality.

A number of difficulties in measuring performance in public service organisations are identified by Haselbekke and Ros (1991) and by Fitzgerald *et al.* (1991). Firstly, it is not easy to identify exactly what is produced in the service organisation. Services may be produced and consumed at the same time so that it is difficult to determine exactly what is produced. Secondly, services are mostly delivered without a price, or it may be difficult to allocate a cost. Thirdly, meaningful comparisons can be difficult because the users of services or the situations to which they apply are not necessarily homogeneous. Fourthly, in assessing the effectiveness of changes made within the organisation, it may be impossible to isolate elements outside the production processes that also have an effect on outcomes. This is particularly relevant in the health sector, where health services are not the only determinant of health status, which is also influenced by individual predispositions and behaviours and socio-economic factors. Haselbekke and Ros also draw our attention to the possibility of resistance from staff and politicians to the introduction of performance measurement in public service organisations.

PUMA/SBO (1999) suggest that certain types of programme lend themselves more readily to performance measurement than others. Services such as health services, which are less tangible and need to be tailored to individual, personal needs and contexts, are more difficult to measure than say, services issuing licences or building roads. They also suggest that programmes such as health services have less scope for calculating price/quality trade-offs and there is the risk that the 'quality side of the equation' gets left in the shadow.

2.3 Defining performance measurement in the health sector

Neely *et al.* (1995) identify three distinct dimensions of performance measurement systems:

1. the individual performance measures
2. performance measurement systems as an entity
3. relationships between performance measurement systems and the environment in which they operate.

Within health systems, performance measurement exists across three levels:

(a) national/system level performance measures

(b) organisational level measures

(c) individual level performance measures.

Performance measures at each level should relate to each other, the key difference between levels being the degree of aggregation. Across the three levels there are several ways to measure performance, including:

- ongoing measurement systems – monitoring
- occasional reviews and evaluation
- *ad hoc* cost/benefit analyses
- client surveys
- benchmarking
- long-term longitudinal surveys (Auditor General of Canada, 1997).

The literature suggests that currently the emphasis in performance measurement in health care is on monitoring services against explicit objectives, and on evaluation – the extent to which programmes actually contribute to desired objectives in relation to the role played by other factors (Auditor General of Canada, 1997). However, there is increasing interest in benchmarking, client surveys and monitoring longer-term outcomes.

The emphasis in this study of performance measurement is on monitoring performance, and although monitoring is closely linked with evaluation, it is outside the scope of this study to look at evaluation in detail.

Although all three aspects of performance measurement are equally important, the focus of this study is largely on performance measurement at the system and organisational levels. This is because performance measurement at the individual level has yet to be established in the Irish health sector. However, reference is made to performance measurement at the individual level where appropriate.

Four key themes can be identified in the literature on the development of performance measurement:

1. the development of performance measurement systems
2. developing data collection systems
3. developing data use
4. co-ordinating performance measurement.

These four themes and the three levels were combined to form the framework for the research, which is presented in Figure 2.1.

Figure 2.1: The Research Framework

The development of performance measurement in the health sector is examined by looking at each aspect of performance measurement across each level of the health system.

Performance level	Aspects of performance measurement			
	System development	Measure definition and data collection	Data use	Co-ordination and collaboration
System-wide				
Organisation				
Individual				

In Chapter 3, the first aspect – the development of performance measurement systems, is explored.

3

The Development of Performance Measurement Systems

3.1 Introduction

The aim of this chapter is to compare the current state of performance measurement in Ireland with approaches taken in a number of other health systems to developing performance measurement systems. The range of approaches currently under development in Ireland is outlined in Figure 3.1.

Figure 3.1: Performance Measurement in the Irish Health Sector

System	Level	Focus
Public Health Information System (PHIS)	National, health board and agency	Public health
Strategy indicators, e.g. national cancer strategy	National and health board	Specific conditions/programmes
Hospital inpatient enquiry (HIPE) system	Agency (acute hospital only) and aggregate for health board	Inpatient activity/case mix
Integrated management returns (IMRs)	Health board and agency	Finance, HR, activity, commentary
Performance indicators	Health board	Service plan objectives, benchmarking

Source: Interview data and reports.

In the performance management system for the health sector as outlined in *Shaping a Healthier Future*, the role of the department is to set/agree national objectives, to evaluate the performance of health boards against those objectives, and to monitor the overall performance of the health system. It states that health boards will need to ensure that adequate structures are in place to measure performance in their own organisations and in executive agencies for which they are responsible.

Currently a range of approaches are being taken to develop performance measurement systems. The service plan is established as the key accountability document between the department and health boards in the Health (Amendment) (3) Act, 1996. Within the annual service planning framework (for further information on service planning see Butler and Boyle (2000)) work is under way to develop performance indicators for inclusion in service plans. An initial set of performance indicators has been agreed by the joint department/health board service planning group, with a small number of indicators for each programme/area. In addition, an inter-board working group has been convened to look at the development of an initial set of performance indicators to be used for comparative purposes across the eight health boards.

Monthly integrated management returns (IMRs) are required from health boards and voluntary hospitals. The main function of the IMRs is to enable the finance unit in the department to monitor and control expenditure and staff numbers across the health sector against allocations set out in the letter of determination at the beginning of each year. Some basic activity data is also included.

The Information Management Unit (IMU) of the department undertook a national study of health status in 1995. This study formed the basis for the Public Health Information System (PHIS) database – a public health minimum dataset. Originally, the focus in PHIS was on mortality rates. The emphasis currently is on developing more composite measures of public health. *Shaping a Healthier Future* (1994) outlined an explicit role for Directors of Public Health within health boards to monitor and report on health status across health board area populations. In line with this move, small area statistics focusing on differences in disease patterns within health boards are being developed to complement the PHIS data. It is anticipated that the PHIS database along with the work ongoing on public health measurement within health boards will allow longer-term health outcomes to be monitored year-on-year and inequalities between and within health boards to be identified and addressed.

At the national level, a number of sectoral/programme-related datasets are being developed. The most advanced of these systems is the hospital inpatient enquiry (HIPE) database. The HIPE system provides demographic, clinical and administrative data on discharge and deaths from acute public hospitals. HIPE data is the basis of casemix analysis and health boards have access to information on their own performance and national performance overall. Datasets are also being developed for programmes/areas such as mental health services, intellectual disability services and physical disability services.

Leahy (1998) reports that accreditation is seen as a way to define and promote quality standards, to identify and share examples of good practice, and to ensure that services meet minimum safety standards. It is reported in interviews that a number of Dublin area hospitals are currently involved in an accreditation initiative on a voluntary basis. The Minister for Health and Children, Micheál Martin, launched the National Teaching Hospital Accreditation Scheme in February 2000, aimed at achieving excellence in quality of care. Initially the accreditation programme will focus on the eight major teaching hospitals in Dublin, Cork and Galway but it is hoped to expand the programme later to include other hospitals and agencies, including private hospitals (*Irish Times*, 2000).

At the organisational level, the Eastern Regional Health Authority (ERHA) implementation taskforce is developing a number of datasets. Initially the main focus in datasets will be on activity, but once established they will be developed more to include other quality and outcome data. For each of five areas – hospitals, intellectual disability services (IDS), community, ambulance and mental health – steering groups have been established to develop performance measurement systems.

Each steering group is made up of representatives from across the range of providers and members of the taskforce provide co-ordination. There is also a data standards working group for each area to advise on the technical aspects of performance measurement.

The interview findings suggest that a considerable amount of activity is ongoing currently to develop performance measurement. While the systems/elements that currently function well and are developed most – HIPE and IMRs – focus mainly on the acute hospital area and on expenditure and activity, further progress on the other approaches under development will provide a more balanced approach to measuring performance. However, community care is the area where performance measurement has yet to be addressed.

3.2 The range of approaches taken to developing performance measurement in other countries

A comparative review of health service reforms across a number of countries shows that there is a clear drive to develop performance measurement. Currently, a range of different approaches is being undertaken, reflecting differences in individual health systems and the organisation of health service provision.

3.2.1 The development of performance measurement systems in Australia

The emphasis in developing performance measurement in Australia is on defining national performance standards, developing performance measures, and making performance data available to decision- and policy-makers at all levels (Australian Government Publishing Service, 1996). The Department of Health and Family Service (DHFS), which has national responsibility for strategic policy for the Australian public health service, is taking the lead at the national level, in line with its corporate vision to promote 'targeted approaches to gain improved outcomes for individuals, communities and the whole population' (DHFS, 1997, p. 6). This will involve promoting planning that is focused on outcomes; working with states and territories to define performance standards and to develop and prioritise performance indicators (PIs); and monitoring and reporting on performance against agreed standards.

The emphasis currently in the development of national performance measurement systems in Australia is clearly on acute health care. The National Health Ministers Benchmarking Working Group (NHMBWG) is working on the development of performance indicators (PIs) in the acute care hospital services sector as in this sector information is more readily available and the use of PIs is more developed. The Australian Council on Healthcare Standards (ACHS), in collaboration with the specialist medical colleges, is developing sets of clinical indicators for use in the ACHS accreditation programmes of acute health care providers. The National Hospitals Outcomes Program commissioned Boyce *et al.* (1997) to examine the range of performance indicators being developed in various health systems and in Australia, and to identify possible indicators of quality of health care and health outcome for use in a national indicator set for acute health care in Australia.

Performance measurement also features strongly in the funding cycle in the Australian health care system. The Commonwealth Health Care (Appropriation) Act, 1998 requires three-year contracts – health care agreements (HCAs) – to be drawn up between the DFHS and the eight states/territories commencing on 1 July 1998. HCAs clearly outline Commonwealth roles and responsibilities and those of the state/territory concerned. These include reporting and sharing information on a regular basis and contributing to the development of national performance indicators with a particular focus on health outputs and outcomes. States/territories are also required in HCAs to supply data and performance information including: the timeliness of responses for requests for data; information sharing with the Commonwealth and other states/territories; and progress on selected high-level PIs.

Future directions in the development of a performance framework are likely to be based on:

- the work of the NHMBWG, which is based around a framework for acute hospital care

- a framework proposed by Boyce *et al.*, which has become widely accepted in Australia and is conceptually different to the above

- current ongoing initiatives in Australia such as the work by the Advisory Group on Quality and Safety in Australian Health Care (NHMBWG report 1999).

3.2.2   The development of performance measurement systems in New Zealand

The funding agreement (FA) between the Ministry of Health and the Health Funding Authority (HFA) is the key accountability document between the centre and regions in the New Zealand health system. A number of *performance expectations* outlined in funding agreements are based on the Crown's Statement of Objectives, each of which includes a number of monitoring requirements. Monitoring arrangements include the submission of quarterly reports and reporting progress against key deadlines. The funding agreement also contains a schedule for sector information, which is largely based around activity and is required on a monthly basis.

The HFA has also selected ten national integrated care demonstration projects for the development of a collaborative framework for health service providers. Each project is focused on health outcomes and has clear objectives and targets against which progress will be measured. Examples given by Borman and Wilson (1998) include:

- a project aimed at reducing inpatient admissions for children with asthma by 20 per cent and improving service delivery for asthma overall

- a project aimed at improving health outcomes for children by 'bridging primary and secondary services for children and developing a single entry and exit point for hospital care'

- a project focused on the management of chronic obstructive pulmonary disease.

3.2.3 The development of performance measurement systems in the United Kingdom

The current National Health Service (NHS) reforms in the UK are focused on providing responsive, high-quality and better-integrated services aimed at reducing inequalities in health and improving the health of the population. *A First Class Service* (NHSE, 1998) outlines a three-pronged approach to improving performance:

1. setting national standards and defining service models, and providing guidance and audit on best practice

2. developing clinical governance to ensure that standards are delivered

3. developing performance assessment. The introduction of the NHS Performance Assessment Framework (PAF) is aimed at monitoring service delivery. The establishment of the Commission for Health Improvement will also underpin the emphasis on quality. The Commission will be responsible for local reviews of services to ensure that systems are in place to monitor, assure and improve quality. An annual national survey of patient and user experience will provide feedback from users on quality issues to be addressed.

The NHS Executive (NHSE) (1999) states that performance assessment is central to all the activities outlined in the reforms. The NHSE outlines a co-ordinating and directing role for itself in the development of the framework, along with a role in monitoring the overall performance of the system. Its key responsibilities include 'the development of better and more useful indicators [and] the encouragement of appropriate action at local level'. A set of high-level performance indicators were 'road-tested' in 1998 and following some amendments were introduced into the system in 1999. The indicators include some clinical indicators. Boyce *et al.* (1997) report that sets of performance indicators for ten common conditions are also being developed by the Department of Health's Clinical Accountability and System Performance Evaluation (CASPE) research group. The high-level performance indicators are outlined in more detail in Chapter 4 of this report.

3.2.4 The development of performance measurement systems in the USA

Performance measurement in the USA has not been driven from the centre to the same extent as in any of the three previous examples, and is built primarily around the accreditation of health care organisations. There are two key players in performance measurement in the American health system. The Joint Commission on Accreditation of Healthcare Organisations (JCAHO) accredits a range of acute, ambulatory and community-type health care organisations. The National Committee for Quality Assurance (NCQA) accredits health plans and HMOs. Both organisations carry out their own on-site evaluations towards accreditation, and while the NCQA has developed its own set of performance measures, the approach taken by the JCAHO is to provide guidance for organisations to select their own performance measurement systems.

In 1999 the JCAHO announced the establishment of a collaborative agreement with the NCQA and the American Medical Accreditation Program (The AMAP is the American Medical Association's organisation for the accreditation of physicians). This agreement is designed to ensure the co-ordination of performance measurement activities across the entire health system. Consequently, the establishment of the Performance Measurement Coordinating Council (PMCC) is aimed at reducing duplication, co-ordinating the development of universal measures, standardising data requirements for different systems, improving data quality, and developing guidelines for the appropriate use of performance data. It is believed that this form of collaboration will also help to reduce the costs of data collection and reporting.

In terms of a performance measurement system, the JCAHO in 1996 announced its vision for a four-pillared approach for the oversight of national quality:

1. the first pillar involves the development of a credible standards-based evaluation framework relating sound processes to good patient outcomes and reducing risk

2. the second pillar involves the development of good measurement systems

3. the capability to evaluate all levels of the system is the third pillar

4. the fourth pillar involves effective co-ordination of evaluation activities and achieving consensus on the best evaluation tools.

The NCQA health plan employer data and information set (HEDIS 2000) measures are included in the comparative review outlined in Chapter 4.

3.2.5 *The development of performance measurement systems in Canada*

The Canadian Institute for Health Information (CIHI, 1998, p. 1) reports that in Canada:

> The capture and dissemination of quality information, through a series of integrated communication systems, is the key to achieving the goals of health reform.

Accordingly CIHI was set up in 1993 to ensure the co-ordinated development of a comprehensive and integrated health system for Canada, with specific responsibility for health standards development and gathering, processing and disseminating health information. In addition, the National Forum on Health, established in 1994, identified the need for better tools to assess population health and the development of evidence-based decision-making supported by an improved IT infrastructure. In 1997 the federal government allocated $50 million towards the development of a Canadian Health Information System (CHIN). CIHI (1998) identifies a number of performance measurement systems being developed at the national level, as follows.

- One of a number of new initiatives developed by Health Canada in support of CHIN is the development of a national health surveillance system to co-ordinate and share information on public health among 400 to 500 institutions linked with disease prevention and health promotion.

- Statistics Canada conducts a National Population Health Survey and produces quarterly reports on population health statistics.

- HEALNet/RELAIS is a multidisciplinary initiative established in 1995 focusing on the development of evidence-based decision support systems. Its brief includes the development of performance indicators for health care organisations and practitioners aimed at quality improvement, achieving greater accountability and addressing problems in information system design to overcome barriers to effective communication across the system.

- CIHI launched the Partnership for Health Informatics/Telematics in 1996, aimed at the 'creation of a non-redundant, non-conflicting set of health informatics and telematics standards for Canada' (CIHI, 1999).

At the provincial/territorial level, CIHI (1998) also reports that health services have become regionalised, with more community-focused regional and local structures replacing traditional institutional governance and management bodies. The shift to community integrated health service delivery models is supported by the development of information systems to integrate and link dispersed care providers, managers and policy-makers, an emphasis on quality improvement, information sharing and improved communication, and the development of outcome measures, best practice guidelines and accountability. Within each province/territory a number of initiatives are focused on developing information systems and performance measurement.

3.3 Conclusion

Currently in Ireland a range of approaches is being taken to develop performance measurement, along similar lines to those across other health systems. The focus of performance measurement across systems is on improving health outcomes, improving the quality of care, achieving national priorities and reducing inequalities in health. Regardless of how performance measurement has developed across health systems to date, the literature suggests that performance measurement systems are largely evolving around:

- developing national frameworks to define standards of expected performance and providing incentives for the achievement of these standards – for example, linking the achievement of standards to funding in publicly funded systems, or to accreditation where services are purchased

- developing good measures and data collection systems

- building managerial capacity to manage performance – for example, clinical governance and benchmarking.

The findings suggest that central leadership is vital in promoting the development of performance measurement and in ensuring collaboration and co-ordination throughout the health system.

The findings also suggest that the development of performance measurement is generally being driven from the centre with national governments taking a lead role in promoting the development of performance measurement and providing incentives or legal frameworks to ensure that health care providers comply with good performance standards. The exception is the USA, where performance measurement has been developed through providing the incentive for health care providers to achieve accreditation.

Performance measurement currently appears to be very focused on acute health care but increasing interest is expressed in looking at other health care settings, in exploring integrated health care models and in building systems around health care outcomes and improvements in population health. In general performance measurement systems are incomplete, with different approaches at various stages of development in various countries. Perhaps the most comprehensive approaches are those being developed in the UK and Canada.

4

Measure Definition and Data Collection: International Experience

4.1 Introduction

In this chapter the second aspect of performance measurement – data collection – is explored in terms of international experience with identifying and defining performance measures and developing systems to collect, aggregate and disseminate data. In the first part of the chapter the focus is on measure definition – dimensions of performance and the types of measures used to capture these dimensions. In the second part of the chapter a framework is developed for assessing comparative practice with regard to data definition and collection.

4.2 Defining and measuring performance

Agreement is required within a health system on what concepts of performance are to be measured and how performance measures are to be defined. The Canadian Institute for Health Information (CIHI) has done a considerable amount of work on data modelling (CIHI, 1999). The development of a national data model in Canada is aimed at describing the data that is needed to meet the information needs of key stakeholders in the Canadian health system, along with common data definitions. CIHI identifies four levels of data – contextual, conceptual, logical and physical – which begin broad in terms of detail and become more focused as they move from contextual through to logical. At the broadest level, contextual data identifies the scope of interest in performance measurement and the major subjects and their relationships. At the next level – the conceptual level – the purpose is to enable a common understanding of each subject and further detail is required to enable each of the major entities to be distinguished. The most detailed level is the logical level where all entities are fully described, the characteristics and permissible values are defined, and all relationships are expressed. This level of detail is necessary to specify information systems. At the fourth level – the physical level – logical data is transformed to show how the data would be stored within an information system, including information exchange structures and formats.

The Auditor General of Canada (1997) suggests that there are four key steps to developing performance measures:

1. defining programme objectives – clear statements of the short-term, intermediate and ultimate results to be accomplished

2. identifying performance indicators – elements or specific aspects of performance to be measured

3. identifying performance expectations – describes the desired level of performance

4. setting performance targets – expressions of expectations in meaningful terms that are challenging but attainable and motivate staff to perform well.

4.3 Issues in measure definition

Three key issues are identified in the literature on recent developments of performance measures: the need to move away from a traditional reliance on financial measures to taking more of a balanced approach; the need to measure what matters; and the need to link performance measures with strategic priorities.

4.3.1 A balanced and integrated approach is required

A focus solely on improving financial performance may encourage short-termism and can have longer-term detrimental effects on the organisation (O'Mara et al., 1998). It is suggested that traditional systems tend to neglect issues such as quality, responsiveness and appropriateness. In the light of such criticisms a balanced and integrated approach to performance measurement is advocated (Ballantine *et al.*, 1998). A balanced approach will ensure that targeted performance reflects the interests of stakeholders in health service performance – patients, the public, managers, professionals working in the service and funders of services. Achieving such a balance will require the management of diverse and conflicting priorities and trade-offs between concepts of performance, through consultation and communication. Such approaches includes the *balanced scorecard* (Kaplan and Norton, 1992), the *performance pyramid* (Lynch and Cross, 1991), and the *results and determinants framework* (Fitzgerald *et al.*, 1991).

Hyndman and Anderson (1997) suggest that public organisations need to move from 'traditional financial concepts' to include the benefits to users, efficiency and other dimensions of performance. They suggest that the current emphasis in performance measurement is on the 'decision-usefulness' of data produced.

4.3.2 The need to measure what matters

PUMA/SBO (1999) and Auditor General of Canada (1997) suggest that the focus in performance measurement has shifted from measuring compliance with processes to measuring results.

> In recent surveys, Canadians have said that they want public servants to focus more on the results to be achieved than on how things get done. They also want to be better informed of the progress that is being made and what they are getting for their tax dollars. (Auditor General of Canada, 1997)

The Auditor General of Canada's (1997) report claims that these demands come at a time when the public want reduced spending on public services but without any reduction in the quality of services, and as governments are looking at ways to deliver more cost-effective services. They claim that the adoption of a focus on results in Canada and the USA has improved results, for example a 13 per cent reduction in mortality following cardiac procedures over eight years in the US Veterans Health Administration.

Some of the more recent performance measurement models emphasise the link between performance and results, for example *the results and determinants framework* (Fitzgerald *et al.*, 1991). Consistent with the increasing emphasis on results, the focus in health has shifted towards the outcomes of health service provision. The thinking is that if the ultimate/primary aim of health care is to improve the health status of the population, progress can only be demonstrated through improvements in health outcomes. However, a number of issues have yet to be addressed in measuring outcomes. Firstly, a number of factors are involved in health outcome, only one of which is health care provision. Secondly, a time lag is involved in interventions that lead to improved outcomes. For example, a successful campaign to reduce smoking will take several years to manifest itself in reduced rates of heart disease and lung cancer. There are also a number of difficulties in measuring outcome.

Although the general view in the literature is that there should be a greater focus on outcomes in performance measurement in the health sector, outputs, processes and inputs are still important in decision-making. Inputs, outputs and processes all contribute to outcomes and need to be measured to avoid what is termed the 'black box effect' – inputs go into the box and outcomes magically come out. For measurement to support decision-making, it is vital to know what happens inside the box so that processes can be refined or inputs adjusted.

4.3.3 The need for strategy-based measures

Performance measurement is advocated as a key mechanism to drive strategy forward at all levels of the system. At the national level, performance measures need to relate to key objectives for health services outlined by national governments. An example of this is where performance expectations outlined in Funding Agreements in New Zealand are required to be based around national objectives outlined in the Crown's Statement of Objectives. This also underpins the integration of national and regional objectives against which performance is judged.

At the organisation level, organisation effectiveness is dependent on the appropriateness of an organisation's performance measures (O'Mara *et al.*, 1998) and the linkages between performance measurement and the organisation's strategy and key success factors (Rangone, 1997). This suggests that both bottom-up and top-down approaches to linking strategic objectives with performance measures are required.

At the individual level, individual performance objectives need also to be aligned with the organisation's strategic objectives so that each individual knows the contribution that they are required to make to the organisation achieving its objectives. Neely *et al.* (1994) suggest that performance measurement can be linked to strategic achievements in two ways – firstly in terms of monitoring implementation and secondly in encouraging behaviour that is consistent with it.

4.4 A comparative review of performance indicators

An overview of the development of performance indicators in health systems is included in the recent CPMR report on service planning in the health sector (Butler and Boyle, 2000). Also included in that report are a number of issues raised in the literature about the development of performance indicators and issues to be considered to ensure the effective use of performance indicators.

For the purposes of this report a comparative analysis of four high-level frameworks was carried out to examine dimensions and understandings of performance, the measures used to capture that performance and the different types of indicators and units of measurement. Further details of measures used in each framework are provided in Appendix 1. While there are differences between frameworks reflecting the various ways in which they are intended to be used within health systems, the comparisons are useful in identifying some of the concepts underpinning performance measurement. The four frameworks compared are as follows.

1. *The NHS Performance Assessment Framework (PAF)*: The NHS PAF is one part of a three-pronged approach to improving performance in the NHS outlined in Chapter 3. In 1998 a number of high-level indicators were 'road-tested' and further refined before being rolled out in 1999. A number of key clinical indicators are included in the framework. Indicators are grouped under six aspects of performance and are intended to be used for comparisons by population group, by condition/client group, and by service organisation.

2. *A National Framework Proposed for Australia*: Neil Boyce and colleagues were commissioned by the National Hospitals Outcomes Program to review critically the development of indicators in Australia and abroad in acute care services and to identify possible indicators to be used for a national set of quality and outcome indicators in Australia. They outline a number of possible indicators under eight categories in their report, along with a number of criteria for the evaluation of potential performance indicators (Boyce *et al.*, 1997).

3. *The HEDIS 2000 Framework*: The HEDIS framework developed by the NCQA is used to measure and report performance in more than 90 per cent of America's health care plans. The latest version of HEDIS will be used by the NCQA in its new accreditation programme (JCAHO, 1998).

4. *The POPULIS Framework*: The Manitoba Centre for Health Policy and Evaluation (MCHPE) developed the Population Health Information System (POPULIS) to provide accurate and timely information to health care decision-makers, analysts and providers and to focus on the link between health and health care utilisation (MCHPE, 1999). Indicators are grouped in eight categories.

4.4.1 Dimensions of performance

There are a number of dimensions of performance in the four frameworks that can be sorted into six key categories: health improvement or outcomes; effectiveness and quality; patient-oriented services; access; financial/resource management; and additional indicators. Table 4.1 examines more closely the explicit dimensions of performance under each of the six categories.

As previously stated, although the purpose of each framework is clearly to measure performance, each is meant to be used in a slightly different way. This is reflected in differences in where the emphasis is placed. For example, the POPULIS framework has a particular focus on health status and is the only one to include sociological/economic and demographic factors possibly involved in health outcomes. The effectiveness/quality and access dimensions are the only categories included by all four frameworks, suggesting that these two dimensions are particularly relevant. The HEDIS framework has a particular focus on financial/resource management and patient-oriented services, whereas these are not included in the POPULIS framework. This reflects the fact that HEDIS is used to review the performance of health plans.

1. *Health improvement/outcomes*

One of the dimensions used in the NHS PAF is health improvement, which is defined as 'the overall health of populations, reflecting social and environmental factors and individual behaviour as well as care provided by the NHS and other agencies'. The measures used for health improvement include: standardised mortality and morbidity; cancer registrations and deaths from malignant neoplasms; deaths from all circulatory diseases; suicide rates; and, deaths from accidents. These measures constitute longer-term population health outcomes. In addition, another dimension – *health outcomes of NHS care* – includes a number of measures focusing on shorter-term outcomes. Several of the measures used are composite measures focusing on premature deaths and avoidable mortality. Some are indicators of inadequate care, such as emergency psychiatric readmission rates and dental decay in five-year-olds. One indicator also relates to adverse events/ complications. POPULIS also includes four broad

Table 4.1: A review of performance measurement frameworks

	National framework – Australia	POPULIS – Canada	Performance assessment framework – UK	HEDIS 2000 – USA
Health improvement/outcomes				
Elective preventive interventions		X		
Health outcomes of care			X	
Health/ill-health		X	X	
Effectiveness and quality				
Effectiveness	X		X	X
Quality		X		
Appropriateness	X		X	
Safety	X			
Technical proficiency	X			
Patient-oriented services				
Acceptability	X			
Patient/carer experience			X	X
Informed health choices				X
Health plan descriptives				X
Continuity	X			
Access				
Access	X	X	X	X
Service utilisation		X		X
Financial/resource management				
Cost of care				X
Health plan stability				X
Efficiency	X		X	
Additional indicators				
Demographic changes		X		
Socio-economic risk characteristics		X		

indicators of health status – premature mortality, life expectancy at birth, low birth weight rate, and disease specific rates.

2. *Effectiveness and quality*

As previously stated, there is a particular emphasis on effectiveness and quality in frameworks. Effectiveness can be seen on two levels – firstly in terms of the effectiveness of the health system, and secondly in terms of the effectiveness of services or care. Boyce *et al.* (1997, p. 15) define effectiveness as:

> The degree to which an intervention produces measurable increases in survival or improved quality of life (or improved outcomes) when applied in routine practice.

For the Australian national framework, Boyce et al. view effectiveness in terms of outcomes of care or outputs – 'outcome-proxies'. They suggest outcomes can be defined by either providers or patients. Provider outcomes include mortality, morbidity and clinical outcomes. Patient outcomes include self-reported outcomes, health status measures, and health-related quality of life measures.

Appropriateness is defined separately from effectiveness by Boyce et al. in terms of 'the extent to which potential benefits of an intervention exceed the risks involved'. The measures of appropriateness they propose for the Australian national framework include case-by-case analysis and the use of proxy indicators of population-based differences in interventions. Two further dimensions relating to effectiveness are proposed by Boyce *et al.*, i.e. *safety* – 'the extent to which potential risks were avoided and inadvertent harm minimised in care delivery processes', and *technical proficiency* – 'the extent to which the performance of interventions by healthcare professionals is consistent with contemporary standards and knowledge of skills relevant to that intervention'. Modular indicators are proposed for both dimensions as opposed to those contained in a national set.

The NHS PAF expresses effectiveness in slightly different terms and more along the lines of an evidence-based approach. Firstly, the measures used reflect the emphasis on evidence-based practice, e.g. composite measures of inappropriately used surgery; composite rates for surgery that is known to be effective when used appropriately, such as CABG (coronary artery bypass graft), PTCA (percutaneous transluminal coronary angioplasty) and hip replacement. Secondly, there are composite measures of hospital admissions for acute and chronic conditions that are 'potentially avoidable hospitalisations' providing retrospective indicators of ineffective care. Thirdly, some of the indicators used for effectiveness also suggest an emphasis on prevention and the early detection of disease – for example, percentage of target population vaccinated and screened for breast and cervical cancer.

The aspects of effective and appropriate care in the NHS PAF are defined as the extent to which services are:

- clinically effective (interventions or care packages are evidence-based)
- appropriate to need
- timely
- in line with agreed standards
- provided according to best practice service organisation
- delivered by appropriately trained and educated staff. (NHSE, 1999, p. 17)

While the performance measures used under *effective and appropriate care* focus on the process of care, the NHS PAF has two further related dimensions focusing on the *health outcomes of NHS care* and *health improvement*.

The NCQA's HEDIS framework also includes a range of *effectiveness of care measures*. Here the focus is on disease prevention and early detection of disease – such as breast and cervical cancer screening, chlamydia screening, prenatal care in the first trimester and check-ups after delivery. There is also a focus on good practice such as controlling high blood pressure, the use of appropriate medications for people with asthma and comprehensive diabetes care. Health outcome measures are not included.

The POPULIS framework does not have a specific dimension for effectiveness. However, a number of measures are outlined under *indicators of quality of care, use of hospital resources*, and *health/ill-health* that can be viewed in terms of effectiveness. They include:

- mortality rates within 30 days of discharge from hospital
- readmission rates within 30 days of discharge from hospital
- rates of 'discretionary' procedures, and for procedures where there is concern about access
- life expectancy at birth and rates for premature mortality, low birth weight and specific diseases
- separations for conditions amenable to good medical treatment, avoidable with good medical care, and conditions sensitive to good ambulatory care.

Vaccination rates and cervical and breast cancer screening are also included.

3. *Patient-oriented services*

The NHS PAF includes the following as a dimension. The patient/carer perceptions on the delivery of services including:

- responsiveness to individual needs and preferences
- the skill, care and continuity of service provision
- patient involvement, good information and choice
- waiting times and accessibility
- the physical environment; the organisation and courtesy of administrative arrangements. (NHSE, 1999, p. 17)

Measures are based around waiting times in accident and emergency departments (A&E), operation cancellations, delayed discharge for people over 75 years, outpatient non-attendances, and percentages for people seen within 13 weeks of GP referral and on waiting lists for 12 months or more.

In the Australian national framework proposed by Boyce *et al.* there are two dimensions relating to patient-oriented services. The first is *acceptability* – 'the degree to which the service meets or exceeds the expectations of informed customers and consumers'. The proposed measurement of acceptability is based around consumer surveys. The second dimension is *continuity* – 'the extent to which an individual episode of care is co-ordinated and integrated into overall care provision'. Measurement is proposed through surveys of patients or their carers to include the success of discharge planning and integration of care.

The HEDIS framework has three dimensions relating to patient-oriented services – *satisfaction with experience of care, informed health care choices, and health plan descriptive information.* Assessment of satisfaction with care is on the basis of two surveys – one for adults and one for children - and there is only one assessment of informed health choices (management of menopause). The health plan descriptive dimension includes a review of the range of additional health plan arrangements for members including arrangements with public health, educational and social service organisations and enrolment measures.

The POPULIS framework is the only one without explicit measures of services designed around patients and their needs and preferences.

4. *Access*

Access indicators are included in each of the four frameworks. Once again with this dimension, differences are apparent in what is understood by access. For example, the NHSE defines *fair access* in terms of 'offering fair access to health services in relation to people's needs, irrespective of geography, socio-economic group, ethnicity, age or sex'. For the Australian national framework, Boyce *et al.* (1997) view access in terms of 'the capacity of individuals to obtain the same quality of service'. Thus the emphasis in the NHS PAF is on the distribution of services and this is reflected in measures centred around access to elective surgery and inpatient services, an NHS dentist, and access to breast and cervical screening. For Boyce *et al.* the emphasis is on providing the same standard of service and this is reflected in measures centred around waiting times for elective surgery, outpatient appointments, the emergency department and emergency admission.

HEDIS measures are based around access to services such as primary care practitioners but also include measures of the initiation of prenatal care and the availability of interpretation services. There are a number of access-related measures in POPULIS relating to access to physicians, access to nursing homes, and the supply and use of beds per 1,000 residents.

5. *Financial/ resource management*

Three of the frameworks have a number of finance-related measures. The HEDIS system includes measures of *health plan stability*, including practitioner turnover, disenrolment, years in business, and indicators of financial stability. It also measures the cost of care including rate trends and high occurrence/high turnover diagnosis related groups (DRGs).

One of the NHS PAF dimensions is *efficiency* and measures include: day case rate; casemix adjusted length of stay; adjusted unit costs for maternity and mental health services; and the percentage of generic prescribing. The only measure of efficiency proposed for the Australian national framework is cost/casemix adjusted separation and they report that none of the measures of 'allocative efficiency' that they reviewed were suitable for a national set.

6. *Additional indicators*

POPULIS has two additional sets of indicators reflecting its status as a population-based framework – *socio-economic risk characteristics* and *demographic changes*. The aim is to provide a better link for decision-makers using the information between health and health care utilisation.

4.4.2 Types of indicator

A number of different types of measure can be identified from the four frameworks.

(a) *Rates*: Rates are used in frameworks to measure, for example, mortality, low birth weight, day cases, suicide, and immunisation. Some rates are adjusted to give more accurate meaning, for example, in the NHS PAF the standardised mortality rate (SMR) is used and elective surgery rates are age-standardised for five procedures. Rates may also be expressed as number per number of residents/population, for example beds or days per 1,000 residents, and admissions to public nursing homes per 1,000 population.

(b) *Averages, means or medians*: A number of measures of central distribution are used such as means, averages or medians. Such measures include average length of stay, waiting times, and average number of decayed, missing or filled teeth in five-year-olds. POPULIS uses median length of waiting times and the NHS PAF uses a casemix adjustment for length of stay.

(c) *Proportions*: Proportions expressed as percentages are used, for example, to measure the percentage of members receiving mental health or chemical dependency services; and percentage of births to women under 20. In the NHS proportions are set out against standards of expected practice. Examples include: percentage of patients seen within 13 weeks of GP referral; percentage of prescribing that is generic, percentage of patients on waiting lists for 12 months or more.

(d) *Costs*: The NHS PAF uses adjusted *unit costs* for maternity and mental health services. DRGs are used in the HEDIS system and Boyce *et al.* propose measuring costs per casemix-adjusted separation.

(e) *Composite measures*: The NHS PAF uses a number of composite measures which are used to assess an element of performance by more than one measure. For example, one measure of the effectiveness of care is a composite of age-standardised rates for five procedures. To assess the health outcomes of NHS care, one measure is a composite, age-standardised measure of readmission rates and surgery rates for hernia recurrence.

(f) *Other measures of performance*: A range of survey approaches are included by Boyce et al. They include case-by-case analysis of the appropriateness of care, surveys of patient satisfaction, and patient-based assessment of continuity. POPULIS includes the use of a socio-economic risk index. Occasionally, descriptive measures are used in frameworks, for example the health plan descriptive information in the HEDIS system.

4.5 Conclusion

This comparative review of high-level performance frameworks examines the range of dimensions of health sector performance targeted and approaches taken to measure that performance. The findings suggest that the key performance issues across the health systems sampled are effectiveness, access, patient orientation of services, efficiency and the outcomes of care, with the greatest emphasis on effectiveness and access. The emphasis in measurement is heavily on quantifying performance and on developing more sophisticated measures such as composite measures. The findings also suggest that there is a growing emphasis on the experience of users and on developing ways to measure this *softer* aspect of performance.

5

Approaches to Data Definition and Collection in the Irish Health Sector

5.1 Introduction

Approaches to defining and collecting data in the Irish health sector were explored through interviews with key individuals involved and through a review of performance measurement systems. Performance measures were reviewed against the issues raised in the comparative review of performance indicators in other countries given in Chapter 4.

5.2 Concepts of performance

The general perception among interviewees is that currently the emphasis in performance measurement in the health sector is on finance and resource management. While this aspect of performance measurement is reported to work well, there was general agreement that performance measurement needs to go beyond the financial to include issues such as quality and to ensure that resources are being used appropriately and effectively. The joint department/health board service planning group recently agreed a set of performance indicators for use in the 2000 service plans. Initially a small number of indicators have been identified for each service area/programme. The intention is that the indicators will be developed and refined further year-on-year. This initial set is encouraging and should move performance measurement beyond financial control and activity measures.

A comparative review was carried out of the performance indicators identified, and HIPE and IMR indicators, using the dimensions of performance identified in Chapter 4. For comparative purposes, the Irish experience is contrasted with that of the other four performance management frameworks in Table 5.1. Further details are presented in Appendix 2.

Table 5.1: A review of performance measurement frameworks

	National framework – Australia	POPULIS – Canada	Performance assessment framework – UK	HEDIS 2000 – USA	PHIS, HIPE, IMRs, PIs - Ireland
Health improvement/outcomes					
Elective preventive interventions		X			
Health outcomes of care			X		X
Health/ill-health		X	X		X
Effectiveness and quality					
Effectiveness	X		X	X	X
Quality		X			X
Appropriateness	X		X		X
Safety	X				
Technical proficiency	X				
Patient-oriented services					
Acceptability	X				
Patient/carer experience			X	X	
Informed health choices				X	
Health plan descriptives				X	
Continuity	X				
Access					
Access	X	X	X	X	X
Service utilisation		X		X	X
Financial/resource management					
Cost of care				X	
Health plan stability				X	
Efficiency	X		X		X
Additional indicators					
Demographic changes		X			
Socio-economic risk characteristics		X			X

5.2.1 Health improvement/outcomes

The public health information system (PHIS) contains data on three types of population health outcome – fertility, mortality (death) and morbidity (illness). A small amount of data is also kept on outcomes of care – caesarean sections, low birth weight and causes of mortality. It is anticipated that the PHIS and national cancer register will enable progress on longer-term health outcomes to be monitored at national and regional levels in the future and will enable closer examination of inequalities in health across the country.

5.2.2 Effectiveness and quality

A clear distinction can be seen between indicators of appropriateness and effectiveness/quality in the service plan indicators.

(a) *Appropriateness*: Indicators of appropriateness generally refer to care settings and their appropriateness in terms of what is known about best practice, for example re-attendances in A&E and OPD and rate of transfer of inpatients in mental health services where treatment in the community is more appropriate. HIPE data includes length of stay, discharge destination and number of day cases by diagnosis related group (DRG).

(b) *Effectiveness/quality*: Three types of indicator relating to effectiveness/quality are seen:

   (i) Indicators of success in increasing the uptake of services, such as immunisation and breastfeeding rates, the uptake of paediatric surveillance and the number of foster carers recruited.

   (ii) Indicators of progress in implementing quality improvement or quality monitoring systems, such as the proportion of cases subject to audit in acute hospitals, and initiatives in services for people with intellectual disability to evaluate the quality of services, client satisfaction and ongoing training of staff.

   (iii) Indicators of adverse quality, such as readmission rates in mental health services and the number of complaints received (although there are issues about the validity of this measure) in acute hospitals.

5.2.3 Patient-oriented services

The findings suggest that the dimension of performance identified in other health systems but neglected in the Irish system, at least at national and regional level, is patient orientation/satisfaction. The need for services to be more clearly focused on the patient and the concept of a patient-focused approach to be reflected in performance management is emphasised in Framework 1 of the *Programme for Prosperity and Fairness* (2000). It suggests that a patient-focused approach would include realigning and reconfiguring services in a way that puts patients first; using feedback from users in the service planning/business planning process and reflecting the needs of users in team and high-level objectives; and developing performance standards to monitor the level of quality of service. It proposes a number of 'key elements of a change programme' as possible indicators of success for the next phase of implementation of the health strategy (see Appendix 3). Examples given include extending hours of service to the public, addressing waiting times, auditing patient satisfaction and improving communication.

5.2.4 Access

Access indicators are used in six of the seven programme areas and more extensively in some than in others. Examples are seen of the concept of access in terms of distribution of services and fair access as in the UK system. Perhaps the best examples are seen in services for older people: the proportion of people assessed as requiring services who actually receive them within a certain time-frame (although the time-frame or how it should be derived is not explicit). Indicators of fair access in primary care include the proportion of targeted school children covered by dental screening, and the proportion of practices having a female GP. In services for persons with intellectual disability an objective is set to identify needs for specialised services and to develop appropriate responses. In services for persons with physical disability data are required on access to additional day and residential places, additional home support services and personal assistants, respite care and additional therapists. However, in this area the measures used could be improved, as discussed later in this paper. The HIPE system contains data on referrals in terms of source of referral, area of residence and GMS status.

Indicators of access in terms of individuals obtaining the same quality of services, as identified by Boyce *et al.* (1997) in Australia, are also included. Examples in the acute hospitals area include waiting times for outpatient appointments and for inpatient admissions, and waiting times in the outpatient (OPD) and accident and emergency departments.

5.2.5 Financial/resource management

Resource management
Data on resource management in IMRs includes expenditure, income, employment and variance against agreed budgets.

Efficiency
Efficiency indicators are found only for child/family services, environmental health and food control areas. Examples include:

- numbers of premises re-inspected and average waiting time for inspection

- proportions of intra-country applications for adoption received that are completed and average waiting time

- proportion of tracing requests completed within 12 months, and average waiting time from receipt of application to commencement of tracing.

Efficiency indicators for environmental health relate to the proportion of premises inspected and target numbers for sampling. IMR data relating to efficiency includes data on bed use, day cases and A&E and outpatient attendance patterns.

5.2.6 Additional indicators

Demographic data
Population profile data for each health board area includes data on age and sex in the PHIS system and data relating to inpatient admissions on age, sex, marital status and area of residence.

Good practice/strategy implementations

A number of indicators are seen relating to the introduction of practices known to be good practice. These include: the introduction of protocols for GP referral in the acute hospitals area, the proportion of children in care with care plans drawn up and reviewed within 12 months, and ring-fencing a proportion of residential beds for acute care discharges. There are indicators relating to the achievement of longer-term agreed objectives such as the implementation of the agreed development programme in services for intellectual disabilities, completion of the 'enhancing the partnership' framework and implementing the recommendations in 'widening the partnership'. In primary care, indicators relate to the establishment of drug misuse databases and, for traveller services, the establishment of a traveller health unit, preparation of plans to enhance service delivery, and for staff awareness training. Indicators relating to the implementation of good practice are also found in mental health services, for example for the appointment of resource persons/liaison officers and the implementation of suicide prevention strategies.

Perhaps the most balanced set of indicators across all categories is in the acute hospital area, and they are further complemented by the measures in HIPE and the IMRs. In Table 5.2 all three sets of data are mapped out along with the data held on PHIS, against the six dimensions of performance identified in the international literature. The findings suggest that performance measurement for acute hospitals is more advanced than in any other service area. Service plan indicators for other areas are patchy and in some areas indicators are skewed – for example the emphasis in child/family services is on efficiency and on access in physical disability services. In addition, for services for physical disability, for older people and for child/family services, indicators are lacking for appropriateness and effectiveness/quality.

It is suggested that data currently collected for acute hospitals could be enhanced as follows in order to improve the decision-usefulness of data:

Table 5.2: Performance measures for acute hospital services

Concept of performance	Performance measure
1) Health improvement/outcomes	*PHIS:* • *Fertility, mortality and morbidity, caesarean sections, low birth weight, causes of mortality*
2) Effectiveness and quality	
a) *Appropriateness:*	• **OPD recall ratio** • **% re-attendances at A&E** • **% acute beds with length of stay > 30 days** *HIPE:* • *length of stay by DRG* • *discharge destination by DRG* • *day cases by DRG*
b) *Effectiveness/quality:*	• **% cases subject to audit** • **Number of complaints received**
3) Patient-oriented services	No examples found
4) Access	• **Waiting times for OPD: % appointments seen within 13 and 26 weeks of GP referral** • **Waiting times for inpatient admissions** • **% patients seen within 30 minutes in OPD** *HIPE:* • *Source of referral, area of residence by county, GMS status*
5) Financial/resource management	

a) *Resource management*	*IMRs:*
	• *Pay, non-pay and income against budget – actual and variance/current month, year to date and projected*
	• *Employment:*
	  – *WTEs and costs by staff category*
	  – *per agency permanent/temporary, full-time/part-time*
	  – *actual/approved levels*
	• *CEO's commentary – financial position, pay/staffing, acute hospitals report, other programmes, outlook*

b) *Efficiency*	*IMRs:* • *Number of inpatient admissions and discharges by speciality/beds available/bed days used* • *Number of day cases per speciality* • *Number of new and return outpatients/patients attending A&E/& for dialysis*
6) Additional indicators	• **Protocols for GP referral**
a) *Good practice/strategic objectives*	• **Management processes for handling patient complaints/feedback**
b) *Biographical*	*PHIS & HIPE: Age & sex, marital status, area of residence*

Note: Proposed service plan indicators are in bold type and HIPE, IMR & PHIS indicators in italics.

- The provision of data on quality and outcomes of care would complement HIPE and IMR data.

- Currently, HIPE data relates to inpatient admissions and one person can account for several data entries. It is suggested that the use of a unique patient identifier would enable individual patients to be tracked on an anonymous basis across the system, and adverse outcomes such as readmission and post-discharge mortality to be captured.

- The addition of a GP identifier would enable referral patterns to be explored.

5.3 Types of measure

The performance indicators identified for use in the service plans for 2000 are a mixture of targets/standards and objectives/strategies to be implemented. Indicators are expressed in a number of ways, as follows.

- *Proportions* – such as the percentage of cases subject to audit. Proportions may be expressed against the total number with assessed needs, against target groups, or against a defined standard.

- *Averages, medians or means* – such as average waiting times. The use of averages alone can be problematic as outliers can balance each other and averages alone do not give any indication of, for example, the proportion of patients waiting for longer than 12 months.

- *Rates* – are used less frequently and examples include readmission rates and immunisation rates.

- *Other measures* – A number of measures relate to objectives to be achieved, such as particular strategies or recommendations. Ratios are used for OPD recall to new attendances. For one particular area indicators relate only to numbers of additional places/services. The difficulty here is that such measures do not provide a specific reference point against which to evaluate the impact of services or progress made. To be useful, these measures need to be expressed against the number of additional places/services required.

The measures used in HIPE are based around activity, use of beds and casemix. They provide information per inpatient admission including information on diagnosis, age and sex, and length of stay. Work is ongoing within the secondary care division to develop costing data to complement activity and casemix data generated through the HIPE system. At the time of writing costs have been matched to 492 diagnostic related groups (DRGs) and 31 hospitals provide data. Clear coding and costing standards have been produced by the casemix working group and data quality is checked before organisations are included in data collection.

The focus of the integrated management returns (IMRs) system is on expenditure control through monthly returns on actual pay and non-pay income and expenditure against that allocated in the organisation's budget. Also required are some basic data on inpatients, outpatients and day cases, along with staff numbers by employment category. The final part of the IMR is the CEO's commentary, where the CEO is required to cover five areas: the financial summary, pay/staffing, acute hospital reports, other programmes, and the outlook. The CEO is expected to focus on approved and anticipated adjustments, extraordinary features of the budget in the year to date, variances in demand-led schemes, waiting lists and bed closures in each consultant-staffed hospital. The CEO is also required to refer to areas not covered in the IMR suite and to provide a forecast position for the organisation for the remainder of the year.

A wide range of measures is used for population denominator and health status in PHIS, ranging from simple measures such as numbers (e.g. numbers of discharges or deaths), rates (such as total fertility and mortality rates), and averages (such as average length of stay). More complex measures include age-standardised measures and 95 per cent confidence limits – some of which are age-standardised.

The national cancer register contains statistics sorted by cancer types. For each type of cancer, patient-related data is recorded on patient area of residence, age, sex, smoking status, marital status, occupation and outcome. Data is also recorded relating to diagnosis and medical treatment. Quarterly reviews published now contain data on survival rates.

5.4 Developing performance indicators

One issue raised by respondents is that performance indicators need to be developed across all health boards to be useful, because their particular use is in terms of allowing credible comparisons. In addition, there is the sense that performance measures need to come up from service areas to ensure that they are relevant, and to ensure ownership to enhance their potential for improving performance. Clearly there are difficulties in achieving a balance between top-down and bottom-up approaches. The forum for the development of performance indicators for service plans is the joint department/health board service planning group. Although the letter of determination asked health boards to include performance indicators in 1999 service plans, this year (2000) is the first time that specific performance indicators have been identified for service plans. Work is also going on within some health boards to develop their own performance measures and an inter-board initiative has been set up to look at the development of a national high-level set of indicators.

Health Canada (1996) suggests that programme 'success indicators' should:

- be results-focused

- be challenging but feasible

- involve a meaningful comparison – over time, with other similar activities or against a reasonable standard

- be measurable and draw on available data and resources

- refer to a result or outcome that can be reasonably attributed to the activity of the programme

- be valid and reliable

- be selective limited to and focusing on key areas of concern

- provide a balanced assessment of programme success

- be useful in evaluations.

The interview findings suggest that there are a number of technical and cultural issues around performance measurement to be addressed. Firstly it is suggested that data systems do not provide sufficient amounts of the type of data that managers require to monitor and improve performance, and second that better use could be made of data that is available, even if this data is only available manually. It was suggested that while the availability of technology *per se* is no longer a constraint, the biggest issue now is the resources to be able to define and direct what needs to be collected at national level. In general those involved in the development of performance measures across the health sector also have a number of other competing responsibilities. It was suggested that there is a growing interest within the department in performance information, and that this now needs to be followed up with a focusing of resources in this area to help define appropriate performance measures.

5.5 Data management systems

All approaches to performance measurement require the availability of good-quality data on performance at all levels of the system. In this section of the report the focus is on how data management (data collection, aggregation and dissemination) systems support and facilitate performance measurement. The general finding is that across the health sector data management systems have to date been underdeveloped. As a consequence, systems are fragmented and there is considerable variation between health boards. The area where data management is most advanced is the acute hospital sector.

It is reported that the type and quality of data in HIPE has improved considerably over recent years and it is generally viewed as being fairly reliable. Nonetheless there are a number of data management issues outstanding on HIPE. Firstly, there is a timeliness issue as data on HIPE is up to six months old before it is available. Secondly, not all hospitals have Patient Administration Systems (PAS) or even where hospitals have a PAS, data on diagnoses are not entered onto the system by practitioners on discharge but by coders up to weeks later. It was suggested that there is a chance that the correct code might not be entered, particularly if the person coding does not know the patient or if the case history is complex.

The picture is very different outside the acute sector. In the community, services are delivered through a complex and dispersed network of providers. Many services are provided by GPs as private practitioners. The bulk of information is recorded manually or is held in patient notes.

The future direction of data management within the department is not clear at this stage, in terms of how data from around the system is collected, aggregated and analysed/interpreted and the findings disseminated to relevant managers throughout the system. Currently responsibility for the collection/aggregation of performance data in the health sector is shared between the department's information management unit (IMU) – PHIS, the department's finance unit – IMRs, the Economic and Social Research Institute – HIPE, and the Health Research Board – intellectual disability and mental health databases. In addition, data comes from the national cancer register and other sources, such as the GMS Payments Board. It was suggested that the current approach is fragmented. One possible way forward under consideration within the department is that one agency should have sole responsibility for data aggregation and the co-ordination of data collection, along similar lines to Canada's independent Information Management Agency.

5.6 Other issues

Several other issues on data definition and collection were identified by interviewees, including the following.

- Performance indicators can only be developed further through being used. It is only by using them and data management systems that areas for improvement are identified.

- Performance indicators are only indicators; they only provide an overview and identify areas for closer inspection.

- GPs are often forgotten in the consultation process in developing performance measures.

- Performance data would be better if based around populations rather than hospitals, with access for health boards.

5.7 Conclusion

The focus of this chapter is on defining performance and appropriate measures, and developing data management systems. Most of the concepts identified from international practice in Chapter 4 are evident in the range of performance measures proposed for use in the Irish health system this year (2000). However, there are two very important observations about the performance indicators chosen for use in service plans, in terms of how the current dataset could be improved. Firstly, a more balanced and comprehensive set of measures is required across the range of service areas. The review suggests that the most comprehensive dataset is that used for the acute hospital sector and this approach could be extended to other areas. In addition there are examples of good indicators in a number of areas that could be shared. The second point raised in the review is that the patient orientation of services is a concept that particularly needs to be developed in the Irish system. This point is stressed in the *Programme for Prosperity and Fairness* (2000), which also suggests some possible ways forward.

In terms of data management, the findings suggest that the approach taken to date to design and develop data systems across the health system has been fragmented and lacks co-ordination. It is suggested that central direction and support is required to improve the integration of data/information systems and facilitate effective communication between all parts of the system.

Building on the findings here, the focus of Chapter 6 is on making the best use of performance data.

6

Developing the Use of
Performance Data

6.1 Introduction

The Audit Commission (1995) estimates that in the UK data collection and use account for about 15 per cent of a hospital's running costs. Yet it sees information as one of the most important resources that a hospital holds. The literature highlights the importance of performance information at all levels of the system: at the policy level, for external monitoring, and for internal use – for managers to assess needs and to plan services, to monitor implementation and the effectiveness and efficiency of services, and for the early identification of problems. At individual level, individuals need to know that they are meeting the objectives set for them and for the service. As such, performance measurement has the potential to drive performance forward. The effective use of performance data relates to both management style and the *decision-usefulness* (Hyndman and Anderson, 1997) of the data. In this chapter of the paper, issues relating to the use of performance data in the Irish health sector are explored, drawing on what is happening in other health systems.

The Report of the Commission on Health Funding (1989) identifies confusion between political and executive decision-making in the Irish health system. It recommends that a clear distinction and separation be made between the two, enabling the political process to concentrate on reviewing the performance of the health services against the criteria of perceived constituent needs and on formulating new policies. The executive function would then concentrate on appraising services against criteria in stated health policies and would be free to make necessary management decisions to ensure that such criteria were met. The report advocates the devolution of responsibility for operational decision-making and monitoring to local level for increased flexibility and innovation, so that decisions can be tailored to local needs and take account of user satisfaction. It highlights the importance of good information for decision-making for managers to plan services and allocate resources, to make choices in the delivery of services and to measure performance on the basis of quality and efficiency.

The Commission on Health Funding identifies three types of information required for decision-making:

- population needs and the capacity of services to meet those needs

- service costs to ensure that resources are allocated and used efficiently

- service outcomes to evaluate the effectiveness of specific treatments and ways in which the services can be delivered to meet needs more effectively.

In terms of performance monitoring and evaluation, the report recommends the establishment of a central function with personnel with the appropriate qualifications and resources, and with responsibility to include monitoring the performance of services in terms of efficiency and quality. The approach proposed in terms of external review is that the performance of organisations should be compared to identify anomalies and unexpected trends – suggesting unusually good or bad performance. Areas of concern would then be followed up qualitatively through peer review and professional audit. One must assume that unusually good performance could also be followed up to identify good practice to be shared.

6.2 The use of performance information in the Irish health sector

A particular issue raised in interviews is the need to develop a culture of using performance data as a management tool and to support decision-making. It is suggested that the emphasis to date within the health sector has largely been on the development of performance systems and measures, with limited focus on developing the capacity to make the best use of data. It is suggested that better use could be made of data than currently, where data is mostly used to look at expenditure and activity. Further it is suggested that there is a need for greater expertise in interpreting and manipulating data, both within the department and in health boards/agencies, and that a co-ordinated approach is required to building skills in data use.

6.3 Developing data use within the department

The use of data within the department needs to be consistent with the changing role of the department and with the principles of SMI. Clearly the types of data required for political and executive decision-making and for operational management are very different. Data required by the department in its policy-making and strategic planning role is high-level, policy-oriented, aggregate data; the data required at regional and organisational levels is more detailed, operationally focused and enables deeper exploration of issues arising – 'drilling down'. Data required to monitor progress and effectiveness at the system level and to ensure accountability between the centre and regions is also different to that required to manage performance at regional and at organisational level. Interview findings suggest that the managerial culture within the department itself needs to focus increasingly on taking a longer-term, proactive and anticipatory approach, supported by good management data.

In line with SMI and *Shaping a Healthier Future*, the department in its leadership role has an important part to play in enhancing governance and accountability across the system and overseeing and promoting the use of performance measurement to enhance management capacity at organisational level. Currently, the secondary care division is focusing on building management capability within hospitals to support the development of performance measurement. It sees building management capability and strengthening governance as an important aspect of developing performance measurement and improving performance.

6.4 Promoting data use at the organisational level

The Auditor General of Canada (1997) highlights a number of examples that it found of ways in which organisations used performance information for decision-making, such as:

- *to improve planning* by using performance data to review and update plans based on results achieved, weaknesses and challenges

- *to focus activity better* by using performance data to focus activities on areas likely to yield the greatest savings

- *to assess policies, practices and regulations* using performance data to assess the implications of proposed changes to policies and practices

- *to assist in resource allocation and reallocation* using performance data to calculate staff requirements and to support requests for additional resources

- *to demonstrate accountability between levels of management and assist in performance appraisal* using performance data to compare achievements with performance expectations

- *to monitor for problems and correct them.*

The findings suggest that currently within Irish health service provider organisations and health boards the use of data is generally limited to financial and personnel control and to monitoring activity. Some health boards have expressed an interest in developing the use of data to evaluate specific services, for example reviews of processes, quality and value for money. However, the findings suggest that greater emphasis needs to be placed on effectiveness, quality and patient satisfaction. In the acute sector it is reported that HIPE data as it currently stands could be complemented with data that could be used by organisations to look at quality issues – such as looking at length of stay in more detail. As previously reported, the HIPE data is considered to be of good quality and to be useful in comparative analysis. It was also suggested that data on waiting lists could be interrogated further, for example by looking at waiting lists by age group and the total length of time that people are waiting, and that health boards have quite a lot of data – which extends beyond the acute sector – that could be better used to review services and to support decision-making.

The findings suggest that for the use of data to manage and in decision-making to be developed at the organisational level, a number of issues need to be addressed. Firstly, managerial culture within organisations has to be receptive to the importance of basing decisions on sound evidence of performance and needs. The Audit Commission (1995) also found this to be the case in the UK:

> The main obstacle to getting better value out of information is that staff seldom understand its value or potential. Their perception will only change if they see the benefits arriving from information, and this means that it must be made more appropriate, timely, accurate and usable. (Audit Commission, 1995, p. 5)

Secondly, individual managers and professionals need to feel empowered and have the appropriate skills and expertise to be able to analyse and interpret data, and to use findings constructively. A third factor is that data be relevant, timely and accessible to those who need it. The issue of relevance is complex, and work is ongoing on the development of performance indicators through a consultative approach is aimed at balancing the needs of divisions within the department with those of health boards and programme managers. Perhaps the most timely data currently is the IMR data, where the time-lag is about six weeks. HIPE data are collected twice yearly with a time-lag of about six months. The difficulties here are that some data (or all data in hospitals where there is not a patient administration system (PAS)) are collected manually and cannot be recorded until the patient has been discharged. However, the time-lag for HIPE has been reduced by half over recent years. In terms of the accessibility of data, the IMU is working on making data available to health boards on CD. On the CD, data relating specifically to the health board is provided along with aggregate data on national rates. At this stage most of the data is based on the PHIS system, but it is intended to extend the data provided year on year.

Fourthly, data must be reliable and known to be reliable so that individuals can have confidence in its use. IMR and HIPE data is said to be reasonably reliable and the quality of data has improved considerably over recent years. Respondents both within the department and in health boards suggested that they have confidence in HIPE and IMR data. However, within the acute hospitals area particular issues were identified with the quality of waiting list data.

The fifth point is that comparability is important in terms of the decision-usefulness of data but it relies heavily on the standardisation of data definitions and on ensuring that data is collected in a standard way across comparators. In addition, organisations must have confidence that they are comparing their own performance with that of similar and comparable organisations. In the acute sector networking is being fostered as a way to develop comparability and the HIPE data is reported to be useful for comparative analysis, once consideration is given to known differences between hospitals. However, it is reported that waiting list data is not comparable because of differences in how individual hospitals define waiting list measures.

6.5 Data use at the individual level

The Audit Commission (1995) undertook a study of information use in acute hospitals. Its report outlined three uses of information in acute hospital settings, which demonstrate how data at the individual practitioner level relates to that used for the management of services:

1. to support clinical decisions – for the management of patient care on an individual level

2. to monitor clinical performance – to audit individual cases and to monitor the quality and outcomes of services

3. to evaluate business performance – to monitor the quality of care including the achievement of standards, to monitor and compare costs, and to meet with statutory requirements.

Individuals need to be aware of what is required of them in terms of performance and how they can contribute to the organisation achieving its objectives. This implies that corporate objectives need to be cascaded down throughout organisations to the individual level. In addition, individuals need regular feedback on how they are doing. Data on performance is also required to inform the appraisal process so that assessments are based on good information rather than hearsay or anecdotal evidence and help to identify ways in which performance can be improved. The *Programme for Prosperity and Fairness* (2000) supports the need to implement an effective performance management system in each public service sector in order to achieve continuous improvements in performance. Interview findings suggest that performance appraisal is very much at the conceptual phase within health boards and service provider organisations. However, some health boards have reported that they are thinking about how performance criteria for individual appraisal and personal development planning can be derived from objectives set out in the service plan.

6.6 Conclusion

Performance data has tremendous potential as a management tool to support decision-making, to enhance accountability and to identify how performance can be improved. However, the findings of this study suggest that performance data is currently under-utilised in the Irish health system and that data use is mainly limited to controlling expenditure and staff numbers. The promotion of data use has largely been overlooked in approaches thus far to developing performance measurement.

7

Co-ordinating Performance Measurement

7.1 Introduction

The literature suggests that co-ordination is vital in any performance measurement system. The recommendations in *Shaping a Healthier Future* (1994) for the future leadership and strategic and policy-oriented role of the department would suggest that the department should take the lead in ensuring a coherent approach to the development of performance measurement at the national level. Three key areas along which performance measurement needs to be co-ordinated are identified in interview findings:

1. the development of a common framework for performance measurement in the Irish health sector

2. preparing the health sector for change

3. system oversight and monitoring.

7.2 Developing a common framework for performance measurement

7.2.1 *Developing structures*

For effective use of performance data the appropriate performance reporting structures need to be in place throughout the system: between the department and health boards, between health boards and all providers, and at the organisational level – between individuals responsible for the delivery of services,

health boards and all providers, and at the organisational level
– between individuals responsible for the delivery of services,
line managers and senior managers. In addition, reporting
structures must be supported by an adequate and integrated IT
infrastructure. It is suggested that a strategic view needs to be
taken on system development across the sector to ensure that
energies are appropriately focused on meeting longer-term
needs and that the various elements being developed are
compatible.

The findings suggest that structures are developed most at
the department/health board level. Currently, performance
management does not explicitly extend to the individual level
and, outside the acute hospitals area, reporting structures are
not so well developed. The community area is probably the area
where most work is required to develop performance
measurement and reporting structures. In the eastern region, the
establishment of the ERHA has provided an opportunity to
build new reporting structures between the department/ERHA
and providers.

The findings also suggest that horizontal structures need to
be developed to ensure that data is used for comparative
analysis of performance. Comparative approaches such as
benchmarking enable organisations to identify priority areas to
be addressed, to learn from each other's experiences and to
spread innovative ways of working. Currently the department's
secondary care division is working with hospitals to build
networks between similar hospital departments for
collaborative working and to foster comparability between
hospitals, and a number of hospitals in the eastern region have
joined together in a voluntary accreditation scheme.

7.2.2 Clarifying appropriate levels of data

Data must be appropriate to the level of the system where it is
used and the way in which it is used. Thus data required
between the department and the health boards is high-level and
related to strategic planning and policy formulation and review,
whereas at the organisational level, more detailed information
is required to support operational management. Performance

measures used at each level must be consistent and they should become more focused as they cascade down to the individual level and more aggregated as they build up to the top level.

7.2.3 Enhancing accountability

For performance measurement systems to work effectively, appropriate levels of accountability throughout the system must be defined. The literature suggests that in real terms, for accountability to be consistent with the emphasis on devolved authority in new public management a shift is required from the traditional management hierarchies to focusing on demonstrating performance against agreed expectations. The Office of the Auditor General of Canada and the Treasury Board Secretariat (AOG/TBS, 1998) identify five principles for effective accountability:

1. clarity of roles
2. clarity of performance expectations
3. balance of expectations and the capacity of each party to deliver
4. credibility and timeliness of reporting
5. reasonable review of performance recognising achievements and necessary corrections – 'closing the loop'.

They also suggest that accountability can be enhanced through an emphasis on developing shared values such as professionalism, honesty and integrity and developing a sense of ownership of results. The need to enhance accountability is an issue raised by the Commission on Health Funding (1989), Dixon and Baker (1996) and *Shaping a Healthier Future* (1994). Accountability is also targeted in the Health (Amendment) Act (3) 1996.

7.2.4 Ensuring the reliability of data collection systems and system security

At national, regional and local level co-ordination is required to assure the *quality of data* collected and the reliability of data collection systems within the health sector. It was suggested that currently in the Irish health sector audit of data collection systems and data entry processes is under-resourced and *ad hoc*. In the health sector information of a very sensitive nature is held on patients. Progressive moves to holding patient information on computerised systems rather than on manual systems makes data increasingly accessible and increases the risk of misuse. Maintaining patient confidentiality and the security of data held on patients is a big issue within the health sector. Ensuring that performance measurement systems comply with security requirements is an important part of system audit. In Scotland the development of a national security and confidentiality policy and the production of IT security guidance at national level, coupled with monitoring information policies at local level, are listed as explicit action points in the Scottish NHS's IM&T (information management and technology) strategy (SHOW, 1998).

7.2.5 Co-ordinating the development of performance measures

It is suggested, both in interview findings and in the literature, that system-wide co-ordination is required in the development of performance measurement on several fronts, as follows.

1. In terms of the development of balanced measures, co-ordination is required to ensure that performance measurement across the system is moving in the right direction and is being driven by the need to measure what matters. The need for performance measurement to move beyond the current emphasis on financial and activity measures to a more balanced set of measures is discussed in Chapter 3.

2. It is suggested that there are significant benefits in a collaborative approach to identifying appropriate performance measures and agreeing data definitions in terms of economies of scale and in pooling expertise and experiences. As Wilson (1992) suggests, there is the need to prioritise performance data to ensure that only the most relevant and useful data is collected. Co-ordination is required to ensure that this is done on a coherent basis at

national and lower levels of the system. Those using the data need to be involved to ensure the relevance of what is collected.

3. Co-ordination is also required at national and regional level to ensure the comparability of data. In terms of the comparability of data, agreement is required on data definitions and to ensure that data is being collected in the same way across providers. In addition, comparisons need to be valid – comparing apples with apples. Bottom-up approaches to measure definition need to be balanced with top-down approaches so that measures are both relevant and comparable.

7.2.6 Integrating and disseminating performance data

In terms of data management, a key role is identified for the department in integrating the data collected and making it accessible to those who need it within the system. Currently the department's IMU is working on the development of CHIPS (casemix HIPE IMR population system) – a compendium of data including IMR data; HIPE; population data; data on casemix, bed designations and waiting lists; and data from the perinatal system. The aim is to bring together data on acute hospitals, which is currently collected through a number of diverse systems.

Various approaches to integrating information, including performance information, are being developed in other countries. In Canada the partnership for health informatics/telematics is developing a Health Information Framework, aimed at providing a coherent structure for 'health information that is collected, stored and disseminated in any format, in any media, for any use, by any stakeholder' (CIHI 1999). Its purpose is to effectively manage information as a 'valuable asset' in health and as an approach to simplify 'the complex world of health information'.

In Australia the National Health Information Development Plan (NHIDP) was launched in 1998 jointly by the Australian Institute of Health and Welfare (AIHW) and the National Public Health Partnership's working group on health information. The NHIDP is aimed at improving the quality, coverage and use of public health information across the Australian health system. The AIHW is an independent national agency established by an act of parliament to provide health and welfare statistics and information. Data is collected at commonwealth, state and territory level and the AIHW's National Health Information Knowledgebase provides integrated access to information (metadata) on a range of health data collections.

In the UK the aim of the NHS Information Authority (previously the information management group) is to improve the ability of the NHS to harness the benefit from the management of information and the use of information technology. It has an explicit role in overseeing the implementation of the NHS's national IM&T strategy, developing standardised data classifications and codes, and developing information management. The NHS's IM&T strategy is aimed at ensuring that quality information is accessible for health professionals to support them in their work and to ensure that planning and management of services is based on good quality information.

7.3 Preparing the health sector for change

7.3.1 Managing change

The literature suggests that part of the national co-ordination role involves leadership to sell the benefits of performance measurement to all stakeholders and to provide appropriate support and advice as required. The Canadian Government in developing its framework for managing results in the public service, focused on developing organisational culture with particular attention to:

- developing credible government-wide support and a supportive culture in departments to reinforce the efforts of programme managers

- developing strong senior-level leadership and commitment

- providing incentives for change and supporting change

- providing training and communications on key concepts, and exchange and sharing of experiences, knowledge and best practice

- developing the capacity within organisations to learn and adapt. (Auditor General of Canada, 1999)

In the UK, the NHS Executive has an explicit role in co-ordinating the development of performance measurement and issues guidance throughout the health system through its regular health services circulars and guidelines. The development of performance measurement has also featured significantly in government white papers on health service reform.

7.3.2 *Ensuring that there are the skills and competencies required to measure performance effectively*

As suggested in Chapter 6, performance measurement needs to be supported by approaches to ensure that there are the skills and competencies required to use performance data, at all levels of the system. The findings also suggest that training is required to promote the importance of performance measurement and its potential in enhancing management capacity. The Office for Health Management is addressing some issues in its Clinicians in Management Programme and, as previously mentioned, the secondary care division is working with acute hospitals to develop managerial capacity. However, interview findings suggest that currently there is a shortage of skills and competencies to interpret performance data and to use existing performance data as an integral part of management, at all levels, both within the department and within health boards/agencies.

7.4 System oversight and monitoring

National co-ordination includes monitoring of the performance measurement system itself to ensure that it is achieving the desired effect – to drive performance forward. This includes ensuring that the system works well and that the appropriate incentives are in place to drive performance measurement forward. Possible misuses of performance measurement are outlined by Boyle (2000), such as:

- *suboptimisation* – the pursuit by managers of their own narrow objectives, at the expense of strategic co-ordination

- *gaming* – altering behaviour so as to obtain strategic advantage, e.g. deferring spending into the future to reduce maintenance costs

- *misrepresentation* – including creative accounting and fraud.

Boyle also highlights some possible results of performance measurement that run counter to the objectives of performance measurement in unleashing managerial capacity. They include:

- *tunnel vision* – concentration on areas covered by performance measures to the exclusion of other important areas

- *myopia* – concentration on short-term issues, to the exclusion of long-term issues which can only be addressed over a number of years

- *convergence* – an emphasis on not being exposed as on outlier against a measure, rather than an emphasis on excellence

- *ossification* – a disinclination to experiment with new or innovative methods.

This view suggests that oversight is required across the system to ensure that the performance measurement system is working well, to minimise the risk of misuse, and to ensure incentive systems are achieving the desired result.

Oversight will also include monitoring performance measures to ensure that they continue to be relevant and valid measures of health service performance. If performance measurement is to drive performance forward, performance measures need to respond to changing needs, changes in priorities or resources and changes in performance itself. The approach put forward in Scotland's NHS IM&T strategy is for review and monitoring of national data collection, taking account of policy changes, information requirements and impact on the services, and at local level to:

- keep collection and demand of data under review to ensure efficiency of means and effectiveness of ends

- ensure that clinical staff are involved in the process of deciding what data is needed and collected

- share appropriate information for re-use, for example Trust data contributing to local planning needs. (SHOW, 1998)

7.5 Conclusion

The findings suggest that the department needs to clarify who is responsible for co-ordinating performance measurement at the national level, and the scope and nature of the co-ordination role. The promotion of performance measurement and national monitoring of the performance measurement system is consistent with the evolving role of the Department of Health and Children. To date the department has had a lead role in developing strategies such as those targeting cancer and cardiovascular disease. In addition, the secondary care division has been developing managerial capacity in the secondary care area. Performance measurement is also promoted through the introduction of performance indicators in service plans, IMRs and the HIPE system. While performance measurement has been progressed over recent years, in large part due to the work of the department, a number of areas where further work is required have been identified in order to build on what has been achieved so far. The findings suggest that the co-ordination role should include:

- ensuring that the appropriate reporting structures are in place

- clarifying appropriate levels of data and how they should be used

- enhancing accountability

- ensuring the reliability of data collection systems and system security
- co-ordinating the development of performance measures
- integrating and disseminating data and information
- promoting change
- system oversight and monitoring.

8

Conclusions and Recommendations

8.1 Introduction

The research findings emphasise the potential that performance measurement has to focus services on achieving results and operationalising strategic and national/regional priorities. Performance measurement also has a vital role in enhancing accountability and supporting reform by enabling devolution of responsibility from the centre to create more responsive services, providing good-quality and accurate data required for effective decision-making, and enabling the impact of policy to be monitored and evaluated. Thus it is not surprising to find that there is growing interest in performance measurement across the range of stakeholders in health systems.

Although there is a considerable amount of work ongoing within the Irish health sector to develop performance measurement systems and performance measures, the focus to date has largely been on the national-regional level, on the acute hospitals sector and on using performance data to control expenditure and staff numbers. While minimum datasets are now being developed for services such as intellectual disabilities, mental health and physical disabilities, performance measurement is largely underdeveloped in the community care area. Recently there has been increasing interest in monitoring health status and health outcomes, and developing the PHIS system. The introduction of service planning and the requirement to include performance measures this year increases the focus on organisations achieving agreed objectives and on the performance of services. The *Programme for Prosperity and Fairness* (2000) requires performance indicators to be put in place for each sector, including the health sector, and to be developed and agreed through the partnership structures established under *Partnership 2000*.

Work to date across the health sector has focused mainly on developing performance measures, with little attention to other equally important areas of performance measurement such as data use. The findings indicate that, particularly outside the acute hospitals sector, better collaboration is required in developing performance measures, using performance data and designing, selecting and developing data management systems. In particular, the findings show that in order to advance further the development of performance measurement, it is vital that energies should be focused on developing a framework for the co-ordination of performance measurement at the national level supported by clear links at regional/organisational and individual levels.

8.2 A framework for performance measurement

The third part of the research brief was to establish the essential elements of a framework for performance measurement. The research examined performance measurement across two dimensions:

• system levels and the purposes of performance measurement at each level

• aspects of performance measurement to be developed.

Across each level, the research focused on the development of performance measurement across four aspects: system development; measure definition and data collection; data use; and co-ordination and collaboration.

8.2.1 System development

On the basis of the findings presented in Chapter 2 it is recommended that performance measurement should occur across three levels in the health sector: the national/system level, the organisation level, and the individual level. Table 8.1

Table 8.1: The performance measurement system in the Irish health sector

Level	Focus	Examples of systems
National/System	• Population health status and health outcomes • Disease-specific mortality and morbidity rates, effectiveness and quality of care • Monitoring of sectoral activity • Monitoring of outcomes and quality of care	• PHIS • National Cancer Register • HIPE, sectoral datasets • Potential, to be developed
Organisational	• Population health status and health outcomes • Demonstrating that health boards are meeting agreed objectives • Health boards ensuring that providers are meeting agreed objectives • Health board financial and staff numbers control	• Small area statistics • Service plan performance indicators • Potential, to be developed – service agreement performance indicators • IMRs, speciality costing
Individual	• Monitoring the contribution of managers and others to achieving organisational, sectoral and national performance objectives	• Potential, to be developed

illustrates the current planned shape of performance measurement in health across the levels, and identifies areas where performance measurement needs to be developed further. Performance data at the national level is required to inform policy decisions and provide information on improvements in population health and the effectiveness of the health system. It also enables issues of national interest to be monitored, such as: inequalities in health between regions; equity between regions in the distribution of resources and access to services; and levels of user satisfaction overall.

At the organisational level, performance measurement enables managers to appraise services against agreed criteria and policies and to make informed decisions on what needs to be done to ensure that the criteria are met. The type of data required at this level is more detailed and operationally focused, and relates to the performance of the organisation overall and the performance of individual services provided. Through comparative analysis of performance data health boards and agencies can find out how they perform against similar organisations and identify areas where their energies should be focused. Performance data at this level can also be used to ensure that organisations work within budget, for example IMR data.

At the individual level, data of a more specific nature is required and relates to the contribution that the individual makes to the organisation. Individual performance objectives need to relate to organisational and national objectives so that they are relevant to the individual in their role and help to drive performance forward. In addition, this sort of data is useful in ensuring that performance appraisal is based on accurate evidence of performance and to identify learning needs to be addressed to ensure that the individual reaches their full potential within the organisation. The findings show that performance measurement at the individual level is clearly an area where attention should be focused in the development of performance measurement systems.

8.2.2 Measure definition and data collection

In Chapters 4 and 5, issues around the development of performance measures are discussed. Drawing on the findings, a stepwise approach to developing performance measures is identified and presented in Table 8.2. It is recommended that the process should begin with broad ideas and become progressively more focused. In initial work in consultation with stakeholders the purposes of a function or a service, or the objectives of a programme, are agreed. Based on the objectives identified, relevant aspects of performance to be targeted are identified. The next stage of the process involves agreeing appropriate levels of performance. The emphasis needs to be on

Table 8.2: *A stepwise approach to defining*
performance measures

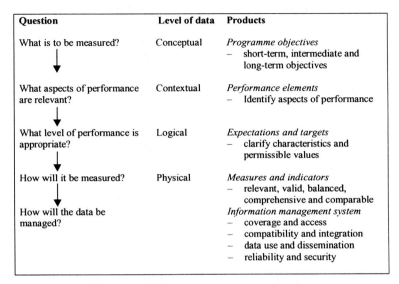

Question	Level of data	Products
What is to be measured? ↓	Conceptual	*Programme objectives* – short-term, intermediate and long-term objectives
What aspects of performance are relevant? ↓	Contextual	*Performance elements* – Identify aspects of performance
What level of performance is appropriate? ↓	Logical	*Expectations and targets* – clarify characteristics and permissible values
How will it be measured? ↓	Physical	*Measures and indicators* – relevant, valid, balanced, comprehensive and comparable
How will the data be managed?		*Information management system* – coverage and access – compatibility and integration – data use and dissemination – reliability and security

achieving a balance between the performance ultimately required and what is achievable within the time and resources available. Targeted performance must result in improvements but may need to be defined in terms of specific stages to be achieved in order to be realistic and achievable. Targeted performance is then expressed in meaningful and measurable terms as performance targets, including measure values, definitions and time-frame.

Once measures have been defined, considerable thought needs to be given to how the data will be managed and to data system design. Consideration is required on the coverage of systems so that data can be entered at the point of service delivery – improving the timeliness of data and reducing the amount of paper in the system. The aim is to ensure that individuals can monitor their own performance and the performance of the services for which they are responsible. Systems should be compatible and integrated so that information can be moved without difficulty and on a timely basis around the health system to those who need it. The reliability of data entry and the maintenance of patient confidentiality are also vital considerations.

8.2.3 Data use

The promotion of data use has largely been overlooked in approaches thus far to developing performance measurement. The findings highlight a number of issues on data use that need to be addressed in order to move the performance measurement agenda forward:

- clarifying the potential use of data with regard to the role that key stakeholders play at each level of the system

- empowering managers to use data and encouraging ownership in performance results

- building managerial capacity at organisational level, addressing training needs and providing the skills and expertise required to analyse and interpret data

- improving confidence in the data by auditing the reliability of data collection systems and addressing comparability issues

- improving the timeliness and accessibility of data to decision-makers at all levels.

8.2.4 Co-ordination and collaboration

The findings indicate that there is a lot of good work going on at present to develop performance measurement but efforts lack co-ordination. A collaborative approach is recommended:

- to share good practice

- for economies of scale

- to ensure the comparability of performance data

- to reap the potential benefits of benchmarking

- to ensure that data systems are compatible.

In particular, the findings show that improved co-operation and information sharing is required within a broad national framework for collaboration. A number of areas where co-ordination should be focused are presented in Table 8.3.

Table 8.3: Co-ordinating performance measurement

Area	Issues to be addressed
Developing structures	• Reporting structures • Strategic development of the IT infrastructure • Developing horizontal structures
Clarifying appropriate levels of data	• Strategic and policy data • Executive and operational data • Data consistency between levels
Enhancing accountability	• Responsibility for results • Developing shared values and ownership
Ensuring reliability of data collection systems and system security	• Ensuring a common understanding of data definitions and how performance is to be measured • Auditing data quality and system integrity
Co-ordinating the development of performance measures	• Promote use of balanced and appropriate measures • Encourage collaboration and pooling of expertise • Prioritise data to be collected • Ensure comparability and relevant comparisons • Ensure that performance measures are consistent with other performance improvement initiatives, e.g. evidence-based practice
Integrating and disseminating data and information	• Compiling data from range of sources • Ensuring accessibility to those who need it and in the appropriate format
Promoting change	• Developing leadership and developing organisational capacity • Ensuring that there are the skills and competencies required for effective performance measurement
System oversight and monitoring	• Ensure that system works well and is not being abused • Ensure that performance measurement is doing what it should and incentives are having the desired effect • Ensure that performance measures continue to be relevant and respond to changes in needs and performance

8.3 Conclusion

There is growing interest in performance measurement in the Irish health system and performance measurement has developed considerably over the past few years. Nonetheless, the findings suggest that a considerable amount of work is still required to build on what has been achieved and for the full benefits of performance measurement to be realised. On the basis of the findings of the study, the key issues to be addressed are:

- clarifying responsibility for overall co-ordination of performance measurement

- extending performance measurement to all areas of the health system

- extending performance measurement to the individual level within organisations and linking it with performance management

- developing more balanced sets of performance measures and ensuring their relevance to stakeholders

- developing an integrated data management system

- ensuring that decision-makers at all levels of the system have the skills and competencies required to make the best use of data produced.

References

AOG/TBS (1998) *Modernising Accountability Practices in the Public Sector: A joint paper – discussion draft.* Office of the Auditor General of Canada and the Treasury Board Secretariat: Ottawa.

Audit Commission (1995) *For Your Information: A study of information management and systems in the acute hospital.* HMSO: London.

Auditor General of Canada (1997) *Report of the Auditor General of Canada.* OAG: Ottawa.

Auditor General of Canada (1999) *Assessing Alternative Service Delivery Arrangements: Discussion paper.* AOG: Ottawa.

Australian Government Publishing Service (1996) *First National Report on Health Sector Performance Indicators: Public hospitals, the state of play.* Australian Government Publishing Service: Canberra.

Ballantine J, Brignall S, Modell S (1998) Performance Measurement and Management in Public Health Services: A comparison of UK and Swedish practice. *Management Accounting Research* (9):71–94.

Borman B and Wilson N (1998) *Outcomes, Indicators, and Community Health Status.* Discussion Paper for the Action for Health and Independence Conference – Information for Action Stream. Ministry of Health: Wellington.

Boyce N, McNeil J, Graves D, Dunt D (1997) *Quality and outcome indicators for acute health care services.* Australian Government Publishing Services: Canberra.

Boyle R (2000) *Performance Measurement in the Local Government Sector.* CPMR Discussion Paper No. 15. IPA: Dublin.

Butler M and Boyle R (2000) *Service Planning in the Health Sector.* CPMR Discussion Paper No. 13. IPA: Dublin.

CIHI (1998) *Navigating the Swirl: An overview of health informatics initiatives.* Canadian Institute for Health Information: Ontario.

CIHI (1999) *Canadian Health Data Model: Draft.* Partnership for Health Informatics/Telematics/CIHI: Toronto.

Commission on Health Funding (1989) *Report of the Commission on Health Funding.* Stationery Office: Dublin.

Comptroller and Auditor General (Amendment) Act, 1993. Number 8 of 1993. Stationery Office: Dublin.

CPMR Briefing Paper No. 1 (2000), *Performance Measurement – A Question of Balance*. IPA: Dublin.

Department of Health and Children (1998) *Working for Health and Well-being: Strategy Statement 1998-2001*. Department of Health and Children: Dublin.

DHFS (1997) *Corporate Plan 1997–98*. Commonwealth Department of Health and Family Services. Commonwealth of Australia: Canberra.

Dixon M and Baker A (1996) *A Management Development Strategy for the Health and Personal Social Services in Ireland*. Department of Health: Dublin.

Fitzgerald L, Johnston R, Brignall S, Silvestro R, Voss C (1991) *Performance Measures in Service Businesses*. CIMA, Gresham Press: Surrey.

Haselbekke AGJ and Ros AP (1991) Performance measurement in theory and practice: Dutch experiences. In TP Hardiman and M Mulreany (eds), *Efficiency and Effectiveness in the Public Domain*. IPA: Dublin.

Health (Amendment) Act (No. 3) 1996. Number 32 of 1996. Stationery Office: Dublin.

Health Canada (1996) *Guide to Project Evaluation: A participatory approach*. Health Canada: Ottawa.

Hyndman NS and Anderson R (1997) *A study of the use of targets in the planning documents of executive agencies*. Financial Accountability and Management 13(2):139–164.

Irish Times (2000) Canadian agency to oversee hospital accreditation plan. 4 February 2000.

JCAHO (1996) *Performance measurement*. Excerpts from Dennis O Leary's 'President's Column', Joint Commission, Perspectives Jan/Feb: 2–3. www.jcaho.org/perfmeas/oryx/dre_pm.htm

JCAHO (1998) *HEDIS 2000 List of Measures*. www.ncqa.org/pages/policy/hedis/ hoomeas.htm

JCAHO (1999) *Nation's Three Leading Health Care Quality Oversight Bodies to Coordinate Measurement Activities*. www.obgyn.net/ENGLISH/PUBS/ announcements/hcq_0520.htm

Kalisch DW, Aman T, Buchele L (1998) Social and Health Policies in OECD Countries: *A survey of current programmes and recent developments*. OECD occasional papers No. 33. OECD: Paris.

Kaplan RS and Norton DP (1992) The balanced scorecard - measures that drive performance. *Harvard Business Review* Jan–Feb: 71–79.

Leahy A (1998) Moving to a quality culture. In Leahy A and Wiley M (1998) *The Irish Health System in the 21st Century.* Oak Tree Press: Dublin.

Lynch RL and Cross K. F. (1991) Measure Up: Yardsticks for continuous improvement. Blackwell: Oxford.

MCHPE (1999) POPULIS : *The Population Health Information System.* Manitoba Centre for Health Policy and Evaluation, University of Manitoba: Manitoba.

Neely A, Gregory M, Platts K (1995) Performance measurement system design: a literature review and research agenda. *International Journal of Operations and Production Management* 15(4):80–116.

Neely A, Mills J, Platts K, Gregory M, Richards H (1994) Realizing strategy through measurement. *International Journal of Operations and Production Management* 14(3):140–152.

NHMBWG (1999) *Third National Report on Health Sector Performance Indicators.* National Health Ministers' Benchmarking Working Group. Commonwealth Department of Health and Aged Care: Canberra.

NHSE (1998) *A First Class Service: Quality in the new NHS.* Government White Paper.

NHSE (1999) *The NHS Performance Assessment Framework.* Department of Health: Wetherby.

O'Mara CE, Hyland PW, Chapman RL (1998) Performance measurement and strategic change. *Managing Service Quality* 8(3):178–182.

OECD (1998) *Performance Measurement.* www.oecd.org/puma/ mgmtres /pac/perform.htm

Programme for Prosperity and Fairness (2000). Stationery Office: Dublin.

Public Service Management Act (1997) Number 27 of 1997. Stationery Office: Dublin.

PUMA/SBO (1999) *Integrating Financial Management and Performance Management.* OECD: Paris.

Rangone A (1997) Linking organisational effectiveness, key success factors and performance measures: an analytical framework. *Management Accounting Research* 8:207–219.

Shaping a Healthier Future: A strategy for effective healthcare in the 1990s. Department of Health (1994). Stationery Office: Dublin.

SHOW (1998) *Addressing the Needs for Information.* www.show.scot.nhs.uk/imt

SMI Working Group on Financial Management (1999) *Financial Management in a Reformed Public Sector.* Dara Design on behalf of the Financial Management Working Group: Dublin.

Wilson C (1992) *QA/CQI Strategies in Health Care Quality.* WB Saunders: Canada.

Appendix I:
Performance measures in four other health systems

---

1. The NHS Performance Assessment Framework
Health Improvement
- Standardised mortality 15-64 years and 65-74 years
- Cancer registrations - age & sex standardised for 7 cancers
- Deaths from malignant neoplasms
- Deaths from all circulatory diseases (under age 75)
- Suicide rates
- Deaths from accidents

Fair Access
- Elective surgery rates - age standardised for 5 procedures
- Weighted size of inpatient waiting list
- Adults registered with an NHS dentist
- Children registered with an NHS dentist
- Early detection of cancer - composite for breast/cervical cancer screening

Effective delivery of appropriate healthcare
- Disease prevention and health promotion -% of population vaccinated
- Early detection of cancer - composite for breast screening age 50-64 & cervical screening ages 25-64
- Inappropriately used surgery - composite, age standardised - D&Cs under 40, grommet for glue ear
- Composite, age standardised elective surgery rates for 5 procedures
- Composite, age standardised admission rates for 3 types of acute conditions expected to be treated in primary care setting - avoidable hospitalisations
- Composite, age standardised admission rates for 3 types of chronic conditions expected to be treated in primary care setting - avoidable hospitalisations
- Mental health in primary care - volume of benzodiazepines
- Composite -cost effective prescribing - 4 criteria
- Composite - discharge from hospital following stroke and fractured neck of femur

Efficiency
- Day case rate
- Casemix adjusted length of stay
- Unit cost of maternity (adjusted)
- Unit cost of care for specialist mental health services (adjusted)
- % of generic prescribing

Patient/carer experience of the NHS
- Waiting in A&E for less than two hours for emergency admission
- Operation cancellations for non-medical reasons after admission
- Delayed discharge for people aged 75 or over
- % of first outpatient appointment for which patients did not attend
- % patients seen within 13 weeks of GP referral
- % on waiting lists for 12 months or more

1. The NHS Performance Assessment Framework continued
Health outcomes of NHS care
- Rate of conceptions age 13-16
- Average number of decayed, missing or filled teeth in five year olds
- Composite, age standardised for adverse events/complications - 28 day readmission rates & rates of surgery for hernia recurrence
- Emergency admissions for people 75 or over
- Emergency psychiatric readmission rates
- Composite infant mortality rates - stillbirths & infant mortality rates
- Composite, age standardised, cancer 5 year survival rates - breast and cervical cancers
- Composite for potentially avoidable mortality for 10 conditions
- Composite, age standardised for in-hospital premature deaths - perioperative mortality & MI aged 50 and over

2. A national framework proposed for Australia – Boyce et al (1997)
Access
- Waiting times for elective surgery
- Outpatient waiting times
- Emergency department waiting times
- Emergency admission waiting times

Efficiency
- Cost/casemix adjusted separation
- None of the allocative efficiency indicators seen were judged to be suitable for a national set

Safety
- None suitable for national set
- Targeted indicators for modules

Effectiveness
- Generic health status indicators
- Balanced indicator sets for modules
- Mortality rates for selected conditions, procedures and investigations
- Unplanned readmission for specific care plans
- Low & very low birth weight

Acceptability
- Surveys of recent acute care patients
- Needs & satisfaction
- Contemporaneous reporting of process & outcome

Continuity
- Patient-based assessment

Technical Proficiency
- Modular indicators for specific clinical conditions, diseases or procedures

Appropriateness
- Cases by case analysis
- Proxy indicators population-based differences in interventions

3. The HEDIS 2000 framework – NCQA

Effectiveness of care
- Childhood and adult immunisation rates
- Breast cancer screening
- Cervical cancer screening
- Chlamydia screening in women (first year)
- Prenatal care in the first trimester
- Check ups after delivery
- Controlling high blood pressure (first year)
- Beta blocker treatment after a heart attack
- Cholesterol management after acute cardiovascular events
- Comprehensive diabetes care
- Use of appropriate medications for people with asthma (first year)
- Follow up after hospitalisation with mental illness
- Antidepressant medication management
- Advising smokers to quit
- Flu shots for older adults
- Medicare health outcomes survey

Access/ availability of care
- Adults access to preventative /ambulatory health services
- Children's access to primary care practitioners
- Initiation of prenatal care
- Annual dental visit
- Availability of language interpretation services

Satisfaction with experience of care
- HEDIS/CAHPS 2.0H, adult and HEDIS/CAHPS 2.0H, child

Health plan stability
- Disenrolment
- Practitioner turnover
- Years in business/ total membership
- Indicators of financial stability

Use of services
- Frequency of ongoing prenatal care
- Well-child visits in the third, fourth, fifth and sixth year of life
- Adolescent well-care visit
- Frequency of selected procedures
- Inpatient utilisation - non-acute care
- Discharge and average length of stay - maternity care
- Casearean section
- Vaginal birth after caesarean section rate
- Births & average length of stay, new-borns
- Mental health utilisation - % members receiving services
- Chemical dependency utilisation - inpatient discharges and average length of stay
- Chemical dependency utilisation - % members receiving services
- Outpatient drug utilisation

Cost of care
- Rate trends
- High occurrence/high cost DRGs

Informed health care choices
- Management of menopause (first year)

Health plan descriptive information
- Board certification / residency completion
- Practitioner compensation
- Arrangements with public health, educational & social service organisations
- Total enrolment by %
- Enrolment by product line (member years/member months)
- Unduplicated count of Medicaid members
- Cultural diversity of Medicaid members
- Weeks in pregnancy at time of enrolment in the MCO

4. The POPULIS framework – MCHPE (1999)

Health /Ill-health
- Premature mortality
- Life expectancy at birth
- Low birth weight rate
- Disease specific rates

Elective preventative intervention rates
- Rate of women with one cervical smear in 3 years
- Rate of flu vaccination to people at particular risk
- Rate of children who receive full immunisation
- Mammography rate for women 50-69

Socio-economic risk characteristics
- High school completion rates
- Unemployment rates
- Mean household incomes
- % female headed households with children
- % births to women under 20
- Socio-economic risk index

Use of hospital resources by residents
- Beds per 1,000 residents
- Days per resident; short stays
- Days per 1,000 paediatric residents
- Separations per 1,000
- Separations for conditions avoidable with good medical care
- Separations for conditions amenable to good medical treatment
- Separations for conditions sensitive to good ambulatory care

Indicators of quality care
- Mortality rates within 30 days of discharge from hospital
- Readmission rates within 30 days of discharge
- Rates of physician contact within 30 days of discharge for medical conditions
- Rates of "discretionary" surgical procedures
- Rates of surgery for procedures where there is public concern re: access

Access to physicians
- Full time equivalent per 1,000 population practising in the area
- % residents with 1 or more contact within the last year
- Visits per 1,000 residents

Access to nursing homes
- PCH beds per 1,000 population
- Residents of PCH per 1,000 population
- Admission to PCH per 1,000 in last year
- Median length of waiting time for admission
- Median length of waiting time in hospital before admission

Demographic changes
- Regional in-migration in the past 5 years
- In-migration/out-migration by important age groups and socio-economic characteristics

Appendix II:
Performance indicators to be included in the service plans for 2000

Indicator	Dimension of performance
Mental health services	
• Rate of transfer of long stay patients from hospital to community care facilities	Appropriateness
• Proportion of inpatients receiving alcohol treatment that may be treated in the community setting	
• Re-admission rates per 1,000 inpatients	Effectiveness
• Number of suicide prevention strategies	Good practice
• Number of appointments of resource persons/liaison officers	
• Measure progress on plans for transfer of acute psychiatric services to acute hospital units	
Child/family services	
• Waiting times for investigation into abuse reports	Access
• Number of foster carers recruited	Effectiveness
• Proportion of children in care with care plan drawn up and reviewed within 12 months	Good practice
• Average length of time to concluded assessment/investigation	Efficiency
• Number of premises re-inspected	
• Average waiting time for inspection	
• Proportion of completed intra-country adoption assessments of applications received	
• Average waiting time to completion of assessment	
• Proportion of tracing requests completed within 12 months	
• Average waiting time from application to commencement of tracing	
Acute hospitals	
• Waiting times for OPD appointments: % seen within 13 and 26 weeks of GP referral	Access
• Waiting times for inpatient admissions	
• % patients seen within 30 minutes in OPD	
• Waiting times in A&E	
• OPD recall ratio	Appropriateness
• % re-attendances at A&E	
• % acute beds with length of stay > 30 days	
• % cases subject to audit	Effectiveness/ quality
• Number of complaints received	
• Protocols for GP referral	Good practice
• Management processes for handling patient complaints/feedback	

Indicator	Dimension of performance
Services for older people	
• % people assessed as requiring home help, paramedical, public health nursing services, day care and respite care and receiving services within a certain time-frame	Access
• % of patients over 65 on waiting lists for ENT, opthalmic and orthopaedic waiting lists < 6 months	
• Number of carers requesting and receiving respite care, and waiting times	
• % people over 75 in residential care	Appropriateness
• Proportion of residential care home beds ring-fenced for acute discharges	Good practice
• Agreements in place between acute and community on admission and discharge protocols	
Travellers' health services	
• Establishment of Traveller Health Unit	Good practice
• Preparation of plans to enhance service delivery	
• Staff awareness training	
Primary care	
• *Dental*	
– % targeted school children covered by screening	Access
– % water fluoridation within statutory limits	Good practice
• *Health promotion*	
– % mothers breastfeeding at birth and at 4 months	Effectiveness
– Proportions of health service staff received training on brief interventions	Good practice
• *GPs*	
– % practices with female doctors	Access
– % vaccination uptake per GMS population	Effectiveness
– % practices with practice nurses	Good practice
– % practices with two or more doctors	
• *Environmental health*	
– % of registered premises inspected	Efficiency
• *Public health nurses*	
– % new-born children visited by PHN within 24 hours of hospital discharge	Access
• *Child health*	
– % uptake of paediatric surveillance	Effectiveness
– Immunisation rates for primary immunisation, boosters & BCG	
• *Drug misuse*	
– Establishment of drug misuse databases	Good practice
• *Food control*	
– Target numbers for sampling	Efficiency

Indicator	Dimension of performance
Persons with intellectual disability	
• Identification of need and development of appropriate responses for more specialised services	Access
• Improve participation of people with intellectual disability in national health programmes and Hepatitis B vaccination programme	
• Initiatives to evaluate quality of services, client satisfaction and ongoing training of staff	Effectiveness
• Implementation of agreed development programme	Good practice
• Completion of 'Enhancing the Partnership' framework implementation	
• Implementation of the recommendations in 'Widening the Partnership'	
Persons with physical disability	
• Number of additional day care places	Access
• Number of individuals receiving additional home support services	
• Number of individuals receiving the services of a personal assistant	
• Number of additional respite places	
• Number of additional residential places	
• Number of additional therapists	
Materials management	
• Measures not reviewed	N/A

Appendix III:
Abstract from the *Programme for Prosperity and Fairness*

Key Elements of a Change Programme for the Health Sector
The next phase of implementation will require a carefully co-ordinated and focused change implementation programme which would have within it, for example, a number of elements, as set out below.

- Extending *hours of service* to the public;

- Co-ordinated action across a broad range of disciplines to achieve specified targets for reduction of *waiting times* and numbers of people waiting for procedures;

- Introduction of a strengthening of *audit of patient satisfaction* within the health care system and the establishment of measurable standards for patient satisfaction;

- Improved *communication* between patients and providers in relation to information on treatment processes, updating of current status, and other relevant information sought by patients and their families;

- Working in partnership with the Service Planning process and co-operating with the ongoing measurement and validation of *performance indicators* as agreed by each agency;

- Achieving a greater *flexibility of skill mix* by utilising a continuum of health care competencies (e.g. developing role of nurse practitioners, nurse-led clinics, etc.);

- Setting clear and measurable targets for the uptake *of vaccination/immunisation programmes*;

- Co-operation in the introduction of *information systems* in the areas of personnel, payroll, attendance, recruitment and superannuation (PPARS);

- Agreed *human resource measures* for a more open recruitment system (as per paragraph 21 of section 1.4), improvements in staff retention, effective deployment of staff, speed of vacancy filling and staff absenteeism, and workforce planning; and

- Co-operating with a comprehensive overhaul of the provisions of personnel policies (circular 10/71) to progress positively the HR agenda in the health service.

These are practical examples of areas in which real progress, resulting in improvements in services for patients, can take place.

Any of these performance measures must, of course, be agreed between the social partners at health sector level. The most suitable vehicle for this would be the partnership arrangements which are now being developed both nationally and locally.

Performance management systems would then operate at agency level where senior management and staff would agree arrangements for setting targets and monitoring outcomes.

(*Programme for Prosperity and Fairness,* 2000, p. 30)

Discussion Paper Series

Discussion Paper 1, *Evaluating Public Expenditure Programmes: Determining A Role For Programme Review*, Richard Boyle, 1997

Discussion Paper 2, *The Fifth Irish Presidency of the European Union: Some Management Lessons*, Peter C. Humphreys, 1997

Discussion Paper 3, *Developing An Integrated Performance Measurement Framework For the Irish Civil Service*, Richard Boyle, 1997

Discussion Paper 4, *Team-Based Working*, Richard Boyle, 1997

Discussion Paper 5, *The Use of Rewards in Civil Service Management*, Richard Boyle, 1997

Discussion Paper 6, *Governance and Accountability in the Civil Service*, Richard Boyle, 1998

Discussion Paper 7, *Improving Public Service Delivery*, Peter C. Humphreys, 1998

Discussion Paper 8, *The Management of Cross-Cutting Issues in the Public Service*, Richard Boyle, 1999

Discussion Paper 9, *Multi-Stream Structures in the Irish Public Service*, Richard Boyle and Michelle Worth-Butler, 1999

Discussion Paper 10, *Key Human Resource Management Issues in the Irish Public Service*, Peter C. Humphreys and Michelle Worth-Butler, 1999

Discussion Paper 11, *Improving Public Services in Ireland: A Case-Study Approach*, Peter C. Humphreys, Síle Fleming and Orla O'Donnell, 1999

Discussion Paper 12, R*egulatory Reform: Lessons from International Experience*, Richard Boyle, 1999

Discussion Paper 13, *Service Planning in the Health Sector*, Michelle Butler and Richard Boyle, 2000

Copies of the above discussion papers are available from:

Publications Division
Institute of Public Administration
Vergemount Hall
Clonskeagh
Dublin 6.
Phone: 01 269 7011   Fax: 01 269 8644
email: sales@ipa.ie